a ses iad carbuncles e lanternes
La sus amunt par grant cel lucerne
par la noit la mer en est plus bele.
e cum il uenent en espaigne la tere.
tut li pais en reluist j esclairet
Jesqua marsille en paruunt les noueles.   AOI.
Gent paiene ne uoelent cesser unkes.
Jssent de mer uenent as ewes dulces.
Laisseno marbrose j si laisent marbrise.
par sebre amunt tut lur nauiries turnent.
A ses iad lanternes j carbuncles.
tute la noit mult grant clartet lur dunent.
a icel iur uenent a sarraguce.   AOI.
Clers est li iurz j li soleilz luisanz.
Clarmindes est issud del calan.
espanelit sest le uair ad estanz.
XVII. rois apres le uint siwant.
cuntes j dux iad ben ne sai quanz.
Suz un lorer kiest en mi un camp.
Sur lerbe uert getent un palie blanc.
V faldestoed uint mis dolifan.
Desur sasiet lipaien baligant.
tut li altre sunt remes en estant.
Lisire dels primer parla auant.
Oiez ore franc cheualer uaillant.
Carles li reis lemperere des francs.
Ne deit manger se io nel li cumant.
par tute espaigne mat fait guerre mult grant.

The Riverside Literature Series

THE SONG OF ROLAND

TRANSLATED INTO ENGLISH PROSE

BY

ISABEL BUTLER

BOSTON   NEW YORK   CHICAGO   SAN FRANCISCO

HOUGHTON MIFFLIN COMPANY

The Riverside Press Cambridge

The Riverside Press

CAMBRIDGE . MASSACHUSETTS

PRINTED IN THE U . S . A

Recat
2/21/68

CONTENTS

LIST OF ILLUSTRATIONS

INTRODUCTION

THE first historic mention we have of a " Song of Roland " takes us back to the year 1066 and the fight at Senlac. Wace, the Norman chronicler, in his account of the battle, says that the minstrel Taillefer, to whom William had granted the first blow, " rode before the Duke on a swift horse, singing of Roland and of Charlemagne, of Oliver and the knights who died at Roncevaux." William of Malmesbury in his " History of the Kings of England " also mentions, though less picturesquely, the fact of the song : " Before the battle, that the men might be encouraged by the martial example of heroes, the ' Song of Roland ' was chanted." Whether this song corresponded to any part of the version of " Roland " that has been preserved in the Oxford Manuscript, we cannot know. But, at least, that version, composed soon after the Conquest, gives us the kind of story the Normans liked to listen to.

The poem is one of those called in Old French a *chanson de geste* ; literally, a song of history, or, more precisely, an epic poem, founded on some historical event and intended to be sung. Long poems of several thousand lines, their form was a ten syllabled verse bound together in stanzas of varying length by a common assonance; that is, the last accented syllable of each line in a given stanza had the same vowel, although the consonants following that vowel need not be the same, as in rhyme. More than a hundred of these *chansons de geste* have come down to us. Among them are some traces of earlier epics or the Merovingians, Charles Martel and Pippin; but of those that have survived the most numerous and important are of Charlemagne and his barons. The " Roland," then, was to the men of the middle ages not an isolated poem, but one of a great epic series.

Poetry in the eleventh century was not " printed an' bound in little books," but was a matter of word of mouth. Quite apart from the learned, Latin literature of the clergy, " it sung itself out in the sun," as M. Gaston Paris has said, " in the streets and squares, on the battlefield, along the highroads, among folk going on pilgrimage, in the doorway of churches, and at the feasts of great lords." Carried through the country by wandering minstrels, chanted to the accompaniment of the viol, the epics told the stories of popular heroes in a language everybody could understand.

The tale was sure to be of battle; sometimes, as in the " Roland," it was the war of Christian against heathen; sometimes that of one of the great feudal lords against another, or against his king. But all alike give us what Stevenson has called "the eternal life of man spent under sun and rain, and in rude, physical effort," at a time when man's chief aim was both how to deal good blows and how to take them. In the stories of Charlemagne, women play little part. Nor do we find anything of the elaborate code of manners of the later poetry of Arthur, or hear of "curteisye" and "vileinye." True, the heroes, as in the later poetry, are always lords and kings; in the "Roland" we hear no word of the common soldier, and only barons have a hand in the battle; but whereas the best of Arthur's Round Table is "the courtliest knight that ever bare shield," the best of Charlemagne's barons is but a good man of his hands. Sir Hector, making lament over Launcelot, says: "Thou wert the goodliest person that ever came among press of knights, and thou wert the meekest man and the gentlest that ever ate in hall among ladies." But Charles's praise of Roland is: "For the arraying and winning of great battles never has the world seen thy like; though I have other kindred none are brave as thou wert."

Oftenest the *chanson de geste* is a long series of warlike adventures, a story for the story's sake; if, as in the "Roland," there are ideas that rule the action of the story, they are the common property of the time: that Christianity is a thing to be fought for with the sword; that "a man should hold him ready to lose both hide and hair in his liege lord's service." Common ideas, but carried in the "Roland" to an heroic pitch. The emotions, too, are the rude, common emotions of daring, say, or of pity. Again and again in the story we see one feeling take possession of a whole body of men. When the Franks crossing the mountains hear the sound of the horn, not Charles alone, but the whole army, "are filled with a strange fear for Roland;" when at Roncevaux they find him dead, "of a hundred thousand men there is not one that does not weep for pity." Such emotion easily spread among the minstrel's hearers. And this poetry that reflected the fighting life of the time was dear to men. It is of value to us to-day because, just as the stories of Arthur give us the ideals of the later, chivalric middle ages, so these stories of Charlemagne give us those of the earlier and ruder middle ages.

A word of mouth poetry, composed by men of little book lore, and sung to those of less, dealing, often, with events of centuries before, could not be accurate; so in spite of their claim to truth, we find in the *chansons de geste* less of history than of legend and imagination. If we look back to history for the beginnings of the "Roland" we find only a name and a fact.

In the year 777, certain Saracens, according to the Annals of Eginhard, came to Charles at Paderhorn and offered to acknowledge him as their sovereign instead of the Caliph of Cordova. The following spring, Charles, with a great army, made an expedition into Spain. He took Pamplona and razed its walls. Then marching south, he crossed the Ebro, and came near to Saragossa; he received hostages of the Saracens, but without taking possession of the city, turned suddenly north. As he was recrossing the Pyrenees, his rearguard was attacked by the Gascons (*i. e.*, the Basques), and in the engagement that followed "the greater part of the officers of the palace, to whom command of the troops had been given, were slain." Here, then, Roland is not even mentioned, but in Eginhard's "Life of Charlemagne" the disaster is given with more detail:[1] "As the army was advancing in the long line of march necessitated by the narrowness of the road, the Gascons, who lay in ambush on the top of a very high mountain, attacked the rear of the baggage train and the rearguard in charge of it, and hurled them down to the very bottom of the valley. In the struggle that ensued, they cut them off to a man; they then plundered the baggage, and dispersed with all speed in every direction under cover of the approaching night. . . . Eggihard, the king's steward; Anselm, Count Palatine; and Roland, governor of the March of Brittany, with very many

[1] Eginhard, Harper's Half-Hour Series, p. 31. The authorship of the "Annals" is disputed, but the "Life" is undoubtedly authentic.

others, fell in this engagement. This ill turn could not be avenged for the nonce, because the enemy scattered so widely after carrying out their plan that not the least clew could be had to their whereabouts."

That is the account given by Eginhard, the secretary and minister of Charles. Opposed to it we have the "Chanson de Roland," preserved in the Bodleian Library at Oxford (No. 23 of the Digby Collection). The manuscript, small and plain, of an inferior quality of parchment and much worn by use, was clearly made not for any great personage, but for the convenience of some travelling minstrel. It is the hasty work of a second-rate Anglo-Norman scribe of the latter end of the twelfth century, who was evidently puzzled by the older dialect he had to transcribe. Of its authorship we know nothing. Language and the internal evidence of names and references seem to show that it was composed between 1066 and 1097, more than three centuries, that is, after the event it describes.[1] Language and reference also show

---

[1] The following illustrate the references generally taken to fix the date between 1066 and 1097 : It is thought that the supposed conquest of England by Charlemagne, mentioned in no other of the *chansons de geste*, was suggested by the recent conquest of England by William of Normandy. Again Charles is said to have established the tribute of Saint Peter in England. The reëstablishment of an old Saxon tax formerly paid to Rome was one of the bribes by which William won the favor of the papacy to his expedition ; at the time of the Conquest it was much in

it a composite story in which the men of more than one French province have had a hand. In it we find the Roland, who in Eginhard is only a name, the hero of an epic of some four thousand lines, and the obscure battle in the Pyrenees changed into a great national defeat followed by a great national victory.

Great as the change is, it does but follow the natural course by which a people turns its history into legend. When a defeat makes the basis of a story, that defeat must be explained, made even glorious. So the Basques, an obscure tribe, drop out of the popular memory, and in their stead we have the old, powerful enemy of southern France, the Saracens. Charles is represented as he was at the end of his reign; instead of the young king of thirty-five, he is the great emperor, the ruler of many lands, full of years and of dignity. The battle is brought about, not by the wit of the foe, as in Eginhard, but by the treachery of one of the Franks, Ganelon. Though the whole rear-guard is lost, the enemy do not escape, as in his-

men's minds, but at another time a French poet would hardly have thought of this tribute. One reason for dating the poem before the crusades is that in it Jerusalem is always represented as in the hands of the heathen. Another is that no use is made of the names of places or peoples with which the crusades familiarized Europe, but the names given to the men of the paynim host are those of the old warfare carried on along the eastern border of Europe between Christian and heathen, in the ninth, tenth, and eleventh centuries.

tory, " under cover of the night," but for Charles
the sun is stayed in the heavens that he may pursue and utterly destroy them. Another victory
is won over a second and yet larger army of paynims, Saragossa is taken, and Charles becomes
master of all Spain.

Yet all this is but the background of Roland,
who, after the manner of epic heroes, has taken
to himself the poetry and the hero-worship of gen-
erations. He is daring, carried to the highest
possible pitch. Like a northern hero of the race
of the gods, he is something more than mortal.
The blast of his horn carries for thirty leagues
through the hills; the weapons of the foe cannot
wound him; when he is about to die there is darkness and tempest in France, a mighty mourning
for the death of Roland. From the obscure Count
of Brittany he has become the nephew of Charles,
the great captain who has conquered many lands
for the emperor, beloved of the Franks and feared
of the Saracens. It is to slay him that the paynims plot with Ganelon the battle; it is through
his daring, his refusal to sound his horn and so
recall the main body of the army, that the rearguard is lost; it is by sounding his horn, though
too late to save himself or his comrades, that the
main body under Charles was made to return. It
is to revenge his death, they pursue and slay the
Saracens crying to them : " Woe worth the day ye
saw Roland." The ivory horn of Roland encour-

ages the Franks to the second battle. After the victory there is no rejoicing, but a hasty return to France followed by the trial and punishment of Ganelon, Roland's betrayer. Thus it is about Roland that the whole story centres.

Nothing is definitely known of the growth of the legend. How it began, whether as short, detached songs, or whether from the first it had epic form, is a matter of dispute among scholars. The theory of M. Gaston Paris is, that soon after the battle of 778 the loss of the rearguard was sung in short songs, called, in Old French, *cantilènes*. These proved particularly popular in the March of Brittany, and the Bretons naturally forgot the Anselm and Eggihard, of whom they knew nothing, but praised their own lord, Roland. Later, the material of these songs was made into a long epic of which Roland was the hero, but which was, undoubtedly, a much less elaborate narrative than that of the "Chanson" of the Oxford Manuscript. This early epic was carried by minstrels into Maine, Anjou, Normandy, and the Isle de France. The Normans, as we have seen, adopted the "Roland," and made it their battle-song at Senlac. In one version Roland appears not as Count of Brittany, but as Count of Mans, a change that would be made only in Maine. It was undoubtedly to please the Angevin Counts that some minstrel introduced a Geoffrey of Anjou into the story, and made the revenger of Roland, Thierry, the brother of Geoffrey. It was probably in the royal domain, the Isle de France, that the kingship of Charlemagne, his feudal overlordship, was so emphasized. Thus in several provinces the story was altered, and retold with fresh detail.

Two stages in the development of the epic may be traced, M. Gaston Paris thinks, in two Latin versions of the story, the so-called "History of Turpin," and a song, the "Carmen de Proditione Guenonis." [1] The History claimed to be by the Archbishop who fought at Roncevaux, and who, in this version, escapes alive. Accepted by the middle ages as genuine, it has been shown by modern scholars to be a compilation of the twelfth century. Though the work is of later date than the "Chanson," chapters xxi–xxix, which give the story of Roland, seem to have had as their source an earlier version of the epic. In this account the Basques have already become Saracens, and the disaster is brought about by the treachery of Ganelon whom the Saracens have bribed. Roland, Count of Mans, and Oliver, Count of Geneva, have been left in command of a rearguard of twenty thousand men and are surprised by fifty thousand Saracens. The Franks destroy the first division of the Saracens, but by the second they are overpowered and scattered. Roland rallies the guard and puts the Saracens

[1] See *Romania*, xi, p. 465, and *Extraits de Roland*, Introduction, p. viii.

to flight, but in the onset loses most of his men
and is himself mortally wounded. Just before his
death he sounds his horn. Charles, on hearing
it, returns, and by the help of the miracle that
stays the sun, pursues the Saracens and utterly
destroys them. Here, then, we find the story of
Eginhard already transformed, although it is far
less elaborate than that of the " Chanson."

In the " Carmen," which also dates from the
twelfth century, we find trace of a third version
that in its detail comes nearer to the " Chanson."
Here we have Ganelon's anger against Roland
given as a motive for his treachery. The Twelve
Peers are mentioned ; the number of the Saracens
has increased ; and the battle is longer. Roland
and Turpin are left alone masters of the field,
and we have the incident of Turpin's blessing of
the dead Peers. The " Carmen " knows little of
Oliver. It is only in the " Chanson " that we get
the contrast between two types of men in the two
comrades. But the " Carmen," with its additions
of which the " Turpin " knew nothing, marks, M.
Gaston Paris thinks, another step in the development of the story by which we to-day remember
Roland.

Mere legend as that story is, it yet has for
us an historic value. By its very failure to give
us the time of the Carlovingians it does, un-
consciously, give us that of the Capetians. The
narrator, like all early story-tellers, paints the

dress, the manners, and customs he saw around him. Even the Saracens, it may be noted, are not distinguished from the Franks by dress or custom, but wear the same armor, fight by the same methods, and have the same feudal organization. But the poem gives us more than the dress of the time. Like any epic story of slow growth it has caught something of the life of the folk who made it. As Homer, better than any history, gives us early Greek life, as Sigurd gives us Odin's North, and as Beowulf gives us the adventurous, sea-loving, Baltic folk, so the "Roland" shows us one side of the life of feudal France when France was leader in Europe. In it we hear nothing of the life of men in hall, but it does reflect for us the energy and the daring of that fighting, feudal society that in 1066 helped to make William of Normandy King of England, and in 1074, Robert of Burgundy Count of Portugal ; reflects, too, the fighting and believing spirit that at the end of that same century, sent men on the first crusade.

Many another *chanson de geste* tells an heroic tale of old war ; that among them all we turn oftenest to the "Roland" is because this had the good fortune to be preserved to us at the happiest moment of its development. It bears the mark of some good workman who knew how to turn to account the good epic material that came ready to his hand. Singularly free from

mediæval digression, turning even the late additions to the story, detached episodes like those of
the calling of the twelve peers of paynimry, or
the story of the death of Aude, to its central purpose, — the praise of Roland, — it has an effective
unity, rare in mediæval stories. Skill there is in
its insistence on the more interesting elements of
the story, as on the comradeship of Roland and
Oliver. Skilful, too, is its use of repetition, the
telling over in two or three successive stanzas
the same idea in slightly different words. In
the later epics this becomes tedious, but in the
"Roland" it is used sparingly, only at the great
moments of the story,—for Roland when he strives
to break his sword, for Charlemagne making lament for Roland, and with the effect, as M. Petit
de Julleville has noted, of the repetition of the
same theme in music. The style, all brevity and
directness, save for this repetition, by its very
simplicity keeps a certain dignity. The story we
are made to feel from the very beginning is a
tragedy; and keeping always, as it does, close to
actual happenings, dealing only with action, not
reflection, it yet contrives, like those older northern
stories of Beowulf and of Sigurd, to give us in its
tragedy the sense of fate.

The popularity of the story in its own day is
attested by its many versions. In France the
form given it followed the taste of the centuries. When, in the thirteenth century, assonance

was held old-fashioned, various rhymed redactions
were made ; but in them minor episodes were
tediously expanded, and the poem lost its old com-
pactness. In the fourteenth and fifteenth centuries, in the days of prose romances, when tales
were beginning to be read, not told, " Roland "
was made a part of a long romance on the son of
Oliver, " Galien." But meantime the story had
spread all over Europe. In the twelfth century
Germany had its " Rolandslied," translated by
the priest Conrad from a version corresponding
to the Oxford Manuscript. The same version,
in the thirteenth century in Iceland, made part
of the " Karlamagnus Saga." Later, the story
spread into Holland, Denmark, and England ; [1]
but it was Italy, always ready to listen to French
minstrels, that most completely adopted it. In
the Library of Saint Mark, Venice, is a manuscript of the poem in a half Italianized French
of the twelfth century. And in the " Reali di
Francia," a fourteenth century compilation from
the *chansons de geste*, Italian boys still read of
Roncevaux.

So the story, in one or another of its many versions, took possession of men's minds, and the
memory of it came often to their lips. " If we

[1] An English translation of the false Turpin, and a fragment
of a fourteenth century translation of one of the later redactions
of the Chanson have been reprinted by the Early English Text
Society.

had another Charlemagne he would find a Roland " was said in France, in the time of that
King John whom the Black Prince defeated at
Poitiers. To Chaucer, a traitor is "a very Ganelon." And it is of the blast of Roland's horn
that Dante thinks, when in the darkness of the
ninth pit of the Inferno, he hears a trumpet "so
loud it turned all thunder faint." Nor was it a
mere bookish memory; to him the heroes of Roncevaux were real; Ganelon he set deep in Hell, and
Roland in the fiery cross of Mars, in the fifth
heaven of Paradise. Again, in the "Mirror of
Perfection," we read that Saint Francis rebuked a
novice, fonder of his psalter than of work with his
hands, with the example of Roland and Oliver,
bidding him remember how they, "pursuing the
paynims with sore sweat and travail even unto the
death, did achieve a victory over them worthy of
all remembrance, and at the last did themselves
die in battle holy martyrs for the faith of Christ;"
adding, with the scorn of the saint for the maker
of books: "yet now be there many that would
fain receive honor and praise of men for only
telling the tale of the deeds they did."

But it is not only in the literature of the time
the story still lives; for beside telling it in
words, men gave it visible form, and wove it into
their tapestries, and carved it on the fronts of their
churches. Many a great lord in France hung
his hall with the story of Charlemagne and his

Twelve Peers.[1] Rudely fashioned, Roland and
Oliver, their long shields before them, stand stiffly
among the carvings of the great doorway of the
Cathedral of Verona. An inscription on the face
of the Church of the Holy Apostles in Florence
boldly tells the twentieth century that, founded
by Charlemagne, the church was consecrated by
Archbishop Turpin in the presence of Roland and
Oliver. In southernmost Italy, in the mosaic floor
of the Cathedral of Brindisi, Charles rides to battle, "his beard spread over his hauberk." And in
Our Lady's Church at Chartres, in the red fire of
one of its windows, Roland still blows his horn,
still smites with Durendal upon the rock. And
we can understand why to Dante Charlemagne
and Roland were among those heroes who "on
earth were of so great fame that through them
every Muse was made rich."

But when the Renaissance came, the stories of
Greece and Rome drove out those of mediæval
France. True, in Italy, in the poetry of Pulci
and Ariosto, the old names of Roland and Oliver
still found a place, but their story was so transformed as to be quite apart from our present purpose. Enough that in the north the song was for
some three centuries forgotten. The age of Louis
XIV knew it not, nor did that of Voltaire. In

[1] Müntz gives these references and many others in his article on
*La Legende de Charlemagne dans l'Art du Moyen Age, Roma-
nia*, vol. xiv, p. 321.

the beginning of the nineteenth century, as part
of the new interest in the middle ages, English
scholars began to talk of the Oxford Manuscript;
and in 1837 Francisque Michel was sent by the
French government to make a copy of it, and, in
the same year, the first modern edition was pub-
lished.   The manuscript was so faulty that much
patient scholarship, much comparison with early
translations and later versions has been necessary
to make it completely intelligible.   Since Michel's
time the poem has been reëdited by many French
and German scholars.   Müller was the first to
establish a good text; but M. Gautier's, accom-
panied by both a line for line translation into
modern French, and much literary and historic
comment, is the most popular, and has passed
through some twenty editions.   After the scholars
followed the translators, Italian, Russian, German,
Danish, English, and again in the nineteenth, as
in the twelfth and thirteenth centuries, the story of
Roncevaux has spread through Europe.   And men
turning back to old tales, add Roland to the good
names of Siegfried, Beowulf, Tristram, Launcelot.

THE SONG OF ROLAND

PART I

GANELON'S TREACHERY

CHARLES the King, our great Emperor, has been
for seven long years in Spain; he has conquered
all the high land down to the sea; not a
castle holds out against him, not a wall
or city is left unshattered, save Saragossa, which stands high on a mountain. King
Marsila holds it, who loves not God, but serves
Mahound, and worships Apollon; ill hap must in
sooth befall him.

*Of Charles's
conquests in
Spain*

King Marsila abides in Saragossa. And on
a day he passes into the shade of his orchard;
there he sits on a terrace of blue marble, and
around him his men are gathered to the number
of twenty thousand. He speaks to his dukes and
his counts, saying: "Hear, lords, what evil over-
whelms us; Charles the Emperor of fair France
has come into this land to confound us. I have
no host to do battle against him, nor any folk to
discomfort his. Counsel me, lords, as wise men

and save me from death and shame." But not a man has any word in answer, save Blancandrin of the castle of Val-Fonde.

Blancandrin was among the wisest of the paynims, a good knight of much prowess, discreet and valiant in the service of his lord. He saith to the King: "Be not out of all comfort.

Marsila takes counsel against Charles

Send to Charles the proud, the terrible, proffer of faithful service and goodly friendship ; give him bears and lions and dogs, seven hundred camels and a thousand falcons past the moulting time, four hundred mules laden with gold and silver, that he may send before him fifty full wains. And therewith shall he richly reward his followers. Long has he waged war in this land, it is mee he return again to Aix in France. And do thou pledge thy word to follow him at the feast of Saint Michael, to receive the faith of the Christians, and to become his man in all honour and loyalty. If he would have hostages, send them to him, or ten or twenty, to make good the compact. We will send him the sons of our wives ; yea, though it be to death, I will send mine own. Better it were that they lose their lives than that we be spoiled of lands and lordship, and be brought to beg our bread.

"By this my right hand," saith Blancandrin, " and by the beard that the wind blows about my breast, ye shall see the Frankish host straightway

NORMAN KNIGHTS CHARGING (BAYEUX TAPESTRY)

scatter abroad, and the Franks return again to their land of France. When each is in his own home, and Charles is in his chapel at Aix, he will hold high festival on the day of Saint Michael. The day will come, and the term appointed will pass, but of us he will have no word nor tidings. The King is proud and cruel of heart, he will let smite off the heads of our hostages, but better it is that they lose their lives than that we be spoiled of bright Spain, the fair, or suffer so great dole and sorrow." And the paynims cry: " Let it be as he saith."

So King Marsila hath ended his council; he then called Clarin de Balaguer, Estramarin, and Endropin, his fellow, and Priamon, and Garlan the Bearded, Machiner, and Maheu his uncle, Joïmer, and Malbien from over- *And sends to him ten am-* sea, and Blancandrin; ten of the fiercest *bassadors* he hath called, to make known his will unto them. "Lords, barons," he saith, "go ye to Charlemagne, who is at the siege of the city of Cordova, bearing olive branches in your hands in token of peace and submission. If by your wit ye can make me a covenant with Charles, I will give you great store of gold and silver, and lands and fiefs as much as ye may desire." "Nay," say the paynims, "of these things we have and to spare."

King Marsila has ended his council. And again he saith to his men: "Go ye forth, lords, and bear in your hands branches of olive; bid

Charles the King that he have mercy on me for the love of his God; say before this first month ends, I will follow him with a thousand of my true liege people, to receive the Christian faith and become his man in all love and truth. If he would have hostages, they shall be given him." Then said Blancandrin: "We will make thee a fair covenant."

And King Marsila let bring the ten white mules the which had been sent him by the King of Suatilie; their bridles are of gold and their saddles wrought of silver. They who are to do the King's message set forth, bearing in their hands branches of olive. Anon thereafter they come before Charles, who holds France as his domain; alack, he cannot but be beguiled by them.

The Emperor is joyous and glad at heart; he has taken Cordova ·and overthrown its walls; The Franks and with his mangonels he has beaten rejoice over down its towers. Great was the plunder the taking of Cordova which fell to his knights in gold and silver and goodly armour. Not a heathen is left in the city; all are either slain or brought to Christianity. The Emperor is in a wide orchard, and with him are Roland, and Oliver, Samson the Duke, and Anseïs the Proud, Geoffrey of Anjou, the King's standard bearer, and thereto are Gerin, and Gerier, and with them is many another man of France to the number of fifteen thousand. Upon the grass are spread cloths of

white silk whereon the knights may sit; and some
of these play at tables for their delight, but the
old and wise play at chess, and the young lords
practise the sword-play. Under a pine, beside an
eglantine, stands a throne made all of beaten gold;
there sits the King who rules sweet France; white
is his beard and his head is hoary, his body is
well fashioned and his countenance noble; those
who seek him have no need to ask which is the
King. And the messengers lighted down from
their mules and saluted him in all love and
friendship.

Blancandrin was the first to speak, and said to
the King: "Greeting in the name of God the
Glorious whom ye adore. Thus saith to
you King Marsila the valiant: much has
he enquired into the faith which brings
salvation; and now he would fain give you good
store of his substance, bears and lions, and greyhounds in leash, seven hundred camels and a thousand falcons past the moulting time, four hundred
mules laden with gold and silver, that ye may
carry away fifty full wains of treasure; so many
bezants of fine gold shall there be that well may
ye reward your men of arms therewith. Long
have you tarried in this land, it is meet that ye
return again to Aix in France; there my lord will
follow you, he gives you his word, (and will receive the faith that you hold; with joined hands
he will become your man, and will hold from you

The coming of the ten ambassadors

the kingdom of Spain "). At these words the Emperor stretches his two hands towards heaven, and then bows his head and begins to think.

The Emperor sat with bowed head, for he was in no wise hasty of his words, but was ever wont to speak at his leisure. When again he raised his head, proud was his face, and he said to the messengers: "Fairly have ye spoken. Yet King Marsila is much mine enemy. By what token may I set my trust in the words that ye have said?" "By hostages," the Saracen made answer, "of which you shall have or ten or fifteen or twenty. Though it be to death I will send mine own son, and you shall have others, methinks, of yet gentler birth. When you are in your kingly palace at the high feast of Saint Michael of the Peril, my lord will come to you, he gives you his word, and there in the springs that God made flow for you, he would be baptized a Christian." "Yea, even yet he may be saved," Charles made answer.

Fair was the evening and bright the sun. Charles has let stable the ten mules, and in a wide orchard has let pitch a tent wherein the ten messengers are lodged. Ten sergeants make them right good cheer; and there they abide the night through, till the clear dawn. The Emperor has risen early, and heard mass and matins; and now he sits under a pine tree, and calls his barons into council, for he would act in all matters by the advice of those of France.

The Emperor sits under the pine tree and summons his barons to council. Thither came Ogier, and Archbishop Turpin, Richard the Old, with Henry his nephew, and Charles calls a council the brave Count Acelin of Gascony, Tedbalt of Rheims and Milon his cousin, and thereto Gerin and Gerier, and with them came Count Roland, and Oliver the brave, the gentle; of the Franks of France there are more than a thousand, and with the rest came Ganelon who did the treason. And now begins the council that wrought so great woe.

"Lords, barons," then saith Charles the Emperor, "King Marsila has sent me messengers: he would give me great store of his havings, bears and lions and leashed greyhounds, seven hundred camels and a thousand moulted falcons, four hundred mules laden with gold of Arabia, more than enough to fill fifty wains; but thereto he charges me that I go back to France, giving his word to come to me at my abiding place at Aix, and there to receive our most holy faith, and to hold his marches of me; but I know not what may be in his heart." "We must bethink ourselves," say the Franks in answer.

Now when the Emperor had ceased from speaking, Count Roland, who is in no wise in accord with his words, stands forth and nay-says him. He saith to the King: "It were ill done to set thy trust in Marsila. It is seven full years since we came into Spain, and for you I have conquered

Noples and Commibles, and I have taken Valtierra and the land of Pina, and Balaguer and Tudela and Sezilie. Now King Marsila was ever a traitor; aforetime he sent fifteen of his paynims, each bearing an olive branch, and they came unto you with a like tale. Then ye advised with your Franks, who counselled you folly; and you sent two of your counts, Basan and Basil, unto the paynims, and thereafter, below Haltilie, their heads were smitten off. Wherefore I counsel carry on the war even as ye have begun it, lead your assembled host unto Saragossa, lay siege to it, even though it be for all the days of your life, and revenge us for those whom the felons slew aforetime."

The Emperor sat with bent head, he stroked his beard and tugged at his moustache, nor answered he his nephew for either good or ill. The Franks are silent, all save Ganelon, he rises and comes before Charles, and speaks right haughtily, saying to the King: "It were ill done to hearken to a braggart — either me or any other — save that his counsel be to thine own profit. When King Marsila lets tell thee he will do homage to thee as thy vassal, and will hold all Spain in fief of thee, and thereafter will receive the faith that we hold, he who counsels thee that thou reject this proffer, recks little, lord, of what death we die. The counsel of pride should not prevail, let us leave folly and hold with the wise."

Thereafter Naymes stood forth — no better vassal was there in all the court — and thus bespoke
the King: "Thou hast heard the answer Naymes advises peace
of Ganelon the Count, and wise it is,
and it be but heeded. King Marsila is spent
with war, thou hast taken his castles, and with
thy mangonels hast beaten down his walls, thou
hast burned his cities and vanquished his men;
when now that he entreats thy mercy, it were
sin to press him further, the more that he would
give thee surety by hostages. (Now send thou
one of thy barons to him.) This great war should
have an end." "The Duke hath spoken wisely,"
cry the Franks.

"Lords, barons, what messenger shall we send
to King Marsila at Saragossa?" And Duke
Naymes made answer: "By thy leave I will go;
give me now the glove and the staff." But the
King answered him: "Nay, thou art a man of
good counsel, and thou shalt not at this time go
thus far from me. Sit thou again in thy place
since none hath summoned thee."

"Lords, barons, what messenger shall we send
to the Saracen that holds Saragossa?" And
Roland made answer: "Right glad were
I to go." "Nay certes, not you," saith Of who should be messenger
Count Oliver, "for you are fierce and
haughty of temper and I fear lest you embroil
yourself; I will myself go, if the King so wills
it." "Peace," the King answered, "nor you

nor he shall go thither; and by my beard which thou seest whiten, not one of the Twelve Peers shall be chosen." The Franks answer not, and lo, all are silent.

Turpin of Rheims then stood forth from the rest and bespoke the King, saying: "Let be thy Franks. Seven years hast thou been in this land, and much travail and woe hath been theirs. Give me, lord, the staff and the glove, and I will go to the Saracen of Spain, and learn what manner of man he is." But wrathfully the King made answer: "Sit thou again in thy place upon the white silk and speak not, save as I command thee."

"Ye knights of France," then said Charles the Emperor, "now choose me a baron of my marches Roland nam- who shall do my message to King Mar- eth Ganelon sila." Then saith Roland : " Let it be Ganelon my stepfather." "Yea," say the Franks, "well will he do your errand; if ye pass him by ye will send none so wise."

Then said the King: "Ganelon, come thou hither, and receive the glove and the staff. Thou hast heard thou art chosen of the Franks." "Sir," Ganelon answered him, "it is Roland who has done this thing; never again shall I hold him in my love all the days of my life, nor yet Oliver in that he is his comrade, nor the Twelve Peers in that they hold him dear, and here in thy sight, lord, I defy them." "Thy wrath is over great," then saith the King, "and certes, go thou must in that I command thee." "Go I may, but without surety, none was there for Basil and Basan his brother.

"Well I know I needs must go unto Saragossa, but for him who goes thither there is no return. And more than that, thy sister is my wife, and I have a son, never was there a fairer, and if he lives he will be a man of good prowess. To him I leave my lands and honours; guard him well, for never again shall I see him with these eyes." "Thou art too tender of heart," Charles answered him, "since I command thee, needs must thou go."

And Count Ganelon was in sore wrath thereat; he lets slip from about his neck his great cloak of sables, and stands forth in his tunic of silk. Gray blue are his eyes, and proud his face, well fashioned is he of body, and broad of chest. So comely he is, all his peers turn to look upon him. And he speaks to Roland, saying: "Thou fool, why art thou in so great wrath? It is known of all that I am thy stepfather, and thou hast named me to go unto Marsila. If God grants me to return again I shall bring woe upon thee so great it shall endure all the days of thy life." "Thou speakest pride and folly," Roland answered him, "and all men know I reck naught of threats. But a man of counsel should bear this message,

Of Ganelon's wrath

and if the King wills it, I am ready to go in thy stead."

"Nay," Ganelon made answer, "in my stead thou shalt not go. Thou art not my man, nor am I thy over-lord. Charles has commanded me that I do his errand, and I will go unto Marsila in Saragossa. But mayhap I shall do there some folly to ease me of my great wrath." At these words Roland falls a-laughing.

When Ganelon sees that Roland bemocks him, so great anger is his he is near to bursting with wrath, and he wellnigh goes out of his senses. He saith to the Count: "Little love have I for thee in that thou hast brought false judgment upon me. O just King, lo, I stand before thee, ready to do thy commandment."

The Emperor holds out to him his right glove, but fain had Count Ganelon been elsewhere, and when he should have taken it, he lets it fall to earth. And the Franks cry: "God, what may this betide? Great woe shall come upon us from this embassage." "Lords," saith Ganelon, "ye shall have tidings thereof.

"And O King," he said again, "I pray thy leave; since go I must, I would not delay." "Go in Jesus' name and in mine," the King made answer. With his right hand he shrove and blessed him, and then he gave him the staff and the letter.

Now Ganelon the Count gets him to his lodging and begins to don his armour, the goodliest he can find; he has fastened spurs of gold upon his feet, and at his side he has girt Mur- Ganelon rid- glais his sword; and when he mounted eth forth Tachebrun his steed, Guinemer his uncle it was, held his stirrup. Many a knight ye may see weep, and they say to him: "Woe worth the day, baron! Long hast thou been in the King's court; and ever hast thou been accounted a man of worship. He who judged thee to go will be nowise shielded or saved by Charles; Count Roland ought never to have had the thought, *for ye twain are near of kin.*" And they say further: "Lord, we pray thee take us with thee." But Ganelon answers: "No, so help me God! Better it were that I die alone than that so many good knights take their end. Ye will return again into sweet France, lords; greet ye my wife for me, and likewise Pinabel my friend and peer, and aid ye Baldwin my son, whom ye know, and make him your over-lord." Therewith he set forth and rode on his way.

As Ganelon fares forth under the high olives he overtakes the Saracen messengers. (They hold on their way and he follows behind,) but anon Blancandrin falls back to ride beside him. Cunningly they speak one to another. "A marvel of a man is this Charles," saith Blancandrin, "he has conquered Apulia and all Calabria; he has crossed the salt sea into England and has

won tribute therefrom for the profit of Saint
Peter; but what would he of us in our marches?"
Quoth Ganelon : "Such is his will; and no man
avails to withstand him."

"The Franks are goodly men," then saith
Blancandrin, "but your dukes and counts do much
Of the talk
by the way hurt to their liege lord in so advising
him; they will bring loss and discomfi-
ture to him and to others." But Ganelon answers
him saying: "In sooth, I know no man save only
Roland who shall be brought to shame thereby.
On a day, as the Emperor was seated under the
shade of the trees, his nephew came to him, clad
in his hauberk — for he was come from the taking
of spoils below Carcassonne — and in his hand he
held a scarlet apple: 'Take it, fair sir,' saith Roland to his uncle, ' for even so I give over to thee
the crowns of all the kings of the earth.' Of a
surety, his great pride must undo him, for each
day he runs in hazard of death ; and if he be but
slain we shall have quiet on the earth."

Then saith Blancandrin : "Fell and cruel is this
Roland who would make all peoples yield them,
and claim all lands for his. But by means of
what folk does he think to win thus much?" "By
the folk of France," Ganelon answers, "for he
is so beloved by them that they will never fail
him; many a gift he gives them of gold and silver, mules and war horses, silk and armour. And
the Emperor likewise has all his desire; for him

Roland will conquer all the lands from here even unto the East."

So Ganelon and Blancandrin rode on till each had pledged other to do what he might to compass the death of Roland. So they rode by highways and bypaths till they alighted under a yew tree in Saragossa. Hard by, under the shade of a pine tree, stood a throne covered over with silk of Alexandria; there sat the King who held all Spain, and around him were his Saracens to the number of twenty thousand; yet not one opened his lips or spoke a word, so eager were they for tidings; and now behold you, Blancandrin and Ganelon.

Ganelon at the Saracen's court

So Blancandrin came before Marsila; he held Count Ganelon by the hand, and he spoke to the King, saying: "Greeting in the name of Mahound and Apollon whose blessed law we hold. We did thy message to Charles, who lifted up both his hands towards heaven, and praised his God, nor made he other answer. But here he sends thee one of his barons, who is of France, and a mighty man, and from him thou shalt hear if thou art to have peace or war." Saith Marsila: "Now speak, for we listen."

Count Ganelon had well bethought himself, and begins to speak with much cunning, as one who is skilful in words, saying to the King: "Greeting in the name of God the Glorious whom we should adore. Thus saith to thee Charles the

mighty: if thou wilt receive Christianity he will
give thee the half of Spain in fee; (the second
half he will give unto Roland, in whom thou shalt
find a haughty compeer.) If thou wilt not accept this covenant (he will lay siege to Saragossa,)
and thou shalt be taken and bound by force, and
brought unto the King's seat at Aix, and thou
shalt be adjudged to end thy days, and there thou
shalt die a vile and shameful death." At these
words King Marsila was sore troubled; in his
hand he held a javelin tipped with gold, and with
it he would have struck Ganelon had his men not
withheld him.

King Marsila·hath waxed red with wrath, and
hath shaken the shaft of his javelin. When Ganelon saw this, he laid a hand on his sword,
and drew it forth from the sheath the
length of two fingers, and spoke to it,
saying: "Most fair and bright thou art; so long
as I wear thee at this King's court, the Emperor
of France will never say I should die here alone
in a strange land, before the bravest have paid
thee dear." But the paynims cry: "Let us stay
this quarrel."

*Marsila is
wroth at the
message*

And the best of the Saracens so besought him,
that Marsila again took his place on the throne.
Saith the Caliph: "Thou hast done ill towards
us in thy desire to smite the Frank. Thou
shouldst give ear and listen to him." "Sir,"
then saith Ganelon, "I must endure it. But not

for all the gold that God has made, nor for all
the treasure of this land will I forego the word, so
I be given leisure to say it, that Charles the great
King has sent by me to his worst foe." Ganelon wore a mantle of sables covered over with
silk from Alexandria, but now he lets it fall to the
earth, and Blancandrin gathers it up; but from
his sword he will not part, he holds it in his right
hand by the golden pommel. And the paynims
say one to another: "Here is a goodly baron."

Ganelon hath drawn near to the King, and
saith: "Thou art wrong to be wroth; Charles
who rules all France lets thee know that if thou
wilt receive the faith of the Christians, he will
give thee half of Spain in fee; the other half shall
go to Roland, his nephew, in whom thou wilt
have a haughty compeer. If thou wilt not do according to this covenant, the King will lay siege
to thee in Saragossa; by force thou shalt be taken
and bound, and conveyed anon to Aix, the King's
seat; neither war horse nor palfrey shalt thou
have for the journey, nor yet a she-mule or he-
mule mayst thou ride, but thou shalt be cast upon
a wretched sumpter; and by a judgment at Aix
thy head shall be smitten off. Our Emperor sends
thee this letter," and therewith Ganelon gave it
into the right hand of the paynim.

Marsila has grown red with wrath; he breaks
the seal and casts away the wax, he looks at the
letter and sees the sum of it. "Charles who holds

France in his power bids me bethink me of his
sorrow and wrath: that is to say of Basan, and
Basil, his brother, whose heads I did let smite off
in the hills below Haltilie. If I would ransom
the life of my body I must send him the Caliph
my uncle, otherwise he will not hold me in his
love." Thereafter spoke Marsila's son, and said
to the King: "Ganelon hath uttered folly. Such
words hath he said to thee it is unmeet that he
live; give him over to me, and I will do justice
upon him." When Ganelon hears him he brandishes his sword, and sets his back against the
trunk of a pine tree.

Now for council the King hath past into his
orchard, and gathered his chief men about him;
The Saracen thither came Blancandrin the hoary-
Council   headed, and Jurfaleu, his son and heir,
and the Caliph, Marsila's uncle and faithful liege-
man. Then saith Blancandrin: "Call hither the
Frank, he has pledged me his faith to our wel-
fare." "Do thou bring him," saith the King.
And Blancandrin took Ganelon by the right hand,
and brought him into the orchard before the King.
And there they plotted the foul treason.

"Fair Sir Ganelon," saith the King, "I was
guilty of some folly toward thee when I would
have struck thee in my wrath. I give thee *as a
pledge* these skins of sable, the border whereof is
worth more than five hundred pounds. Before to-
morrow at evening a fair amend shall be thine."

"I will not refuse it," Ganelon answered him, "and may it please God give thee good thanks."

Then quoth Marsila: "Ganelon, in good faith I have it in my heart to love thee well. Tell me now of Charlemagne. Methinks, he is of great age and has outlived his time, for I deem him more than two hundred years old. Through many lands has he jour-neyed, and many a blow has he taken on his em-bossed shield, and many a mighty king has he brought low; when will he yield him in the strife?" "Nay, not such is Charles," Ganelon answered him: "Whosoever looks on the Em-peror, or knows him, must account him a man of much prowess. I know not how to praise and glorify him to the full sum of his honour and bounty. Who can reckon his worth? and God has gifted him with such valour that rather had he die than give up his lordship."

Marsila would know of Charles

Quoth the paynim: "Much I marvel at this Charles who is old and hoary; two hundred years and more he is, methinks. Through many lands has he travelled, and has taken many a thrust of lance and spear, and many a mighty king has he brought low; when will he yield him in the strife?" "That will never be," saith Ganelon, "so long as his nephew is a living man, he hath not his fellow for courage under the cope of hea-ven; and Oliver his comrade is of good prowess, and likewise the Twelve Peers whom Charles holds right dear; they, together with twenty thousand knights, make up the vanguard; and Charles is safe and unafraid."

Saith the paynim: "Greatly I marvel at this Charles who is white-headed and hoary, methinks he is two hundred years and more. Through many lands has he ridden a conqueror, many a blow has he taken from good spears and sharp; when will he yield him in the strife?" "That will never be," quoth Ganelon, "so long as Roland is a living man, he hath not his like in courage from here even unto the East; and Oliver, his comrade, is right valiant, and the Twelve Peers whom Charles holds so dear, they, together with twenty thousand Franks, make up the vanguard. Secure is Charles and fearful of no man living."

"Fair Sir Ganelon," thus saith King Marsila, "a fairer folk than mine ye shall not see; I have upon four hundred thousand knights, with them I may well do battle against Charles and his Franks." "Nay, not at this time," Ganelon answers him, "or great will be the slaughter of thy paynims. Leave thou folly and seek after wisdom; give such store of thy substance unto the Emperor that there will be no Frank that does not marvel thereat; send him thereto twenty hostages, and the King will return again into fair France; but his rearguard he will leave behind him, and in it, of a surety, will be Count Roland, his nephew, and Oliver the

Ganelon offers counsel

valiant, the courteous: and both counts shall be slain, if thou wilt put thy trust in me. And the great pride of Charles shall come to its fall, and thenceforth he will have no desire to wage more war upon thee."

"Fair Sir Ganelon," then saith King Marsila, "how may I slay this Roland?" Quoth Ganelon: "Even that will I tell thee. The King will be at the main pass of Cizre, and he will have set his rearguard behind him; in it will be the mighty Count Roland, his nephew, and Oliver, in whom he sets his trust, and in their company will be twenty thousand Franks. But do thou send against them one hundred thou- The great treason sand of thy paynims, and do them battle a first time, that the men of France may be smitten and sore hurt. Now mayhap, in this first stour, thine own may be slain with great slaughter, but do thou set upon the Franks a second time, with like array, that Roland may in no wise escape. And for thy part thou wilt have done a noble deed of arms, and thou shalt be untroubled by war all the days of thy life.

" Whosoever may compass the death of Roland in that place will thereby smite off the right arm of Charles; his great armies will have an end, never again shall he call together such hosts, and the Great Land shall have peace." When Marsila heard this saying he kissed Ganelon upon the neck; then he began to open his treasures.

Quoth Marsila: "What need of more words? No counsel is good in which a man may not set his trust. Now do thou therefore swear me straight the treason (that I shall find Roland in the rearguard.") "Let it be as thou wilt," said Ganelon: and he swore the treason upon the relics in his sword Murglais, and therewith became a traitor.

Hard by, was a throne wrought of ivory, and to it Marsila let bring a book wherein was writ the law of Mahound and Tervagant, and upon it the Saracen of Spain swore that if he found Roland in the rearguard, he would set upon him with all his folk, and if that he might, forthwith slay him. "Blessed be our covenant," quoth Ganelon.

Thereupon came thither a paynim called Valdabrun, who aforetime had stood godfather to King Marsila; fair and laughing, he said to Ganelon: "Take thou my sword, no man weareth a better, and between the guards thereof are more than a thousand mangons. I give it thee, fair sir, in all friendship, but do thou aid us against Roland the baron, and take heed that we find him in the rearguard." "So shall it be," quoth Count Ganelon; and each kissed other on the cheek and the chin.

Ganelon receiveth gifts

Thereafter came thither a paynim hight Climborin, frank and free, he said to Ganelon: "Take thou my helm, a better was never seen, but do thou help us against Roland Lord of the Marches,

in such wise that we may bring him to shame."
"Even so will I do," saith Ganelon; and each
kissed other on the cheek and the mouth.

Then thither came Bramimonde the Queen, and
saith to the Count: "Sir, thou art right dear to
me, in that thou art beloved of my lord and all his
men. To thy wife I would send these two bracelets, well seen are they with jacinth and gold and
amethysts, and they are of a greater price than
all the riches of Rome, thy Emperor hath none so
goodly." And Ganelon takes the bracelets and
bestows them in his boot.

Then the King calls Malduit his treasurer,
saying: "Hast thou made ready the gifts for
Charles?" "Yea, lord," he answers, "all is ready,
— seven hundred camels laden with gold and silver, and twenty hostages, the noblest under heaven."

Marsila lays a hand on Ganelon's shoulder and
speaks to him, saying: "A goodly baron and
wise thou art, but by that faith thou deemest
most holy, have a heed that thou turn not thy
heart from us; and I will give thee great store of
my substance, ten mules laden with the finest
gold of Arabia; and each year thou shalt have a
like gift. Now take thou the keys of this great
city, and convey thou to Charles the rich gifts,
(and give over to him from me the twenty hostages:) but thereafter have a care the rearguard
be adjudged to Roland. And so be it I may come

upon him in pass or defile, I will do him battle
to the death." "Methinks I tarry too long,"
saith Ganelon in answer; and therewith he
mounts his horse and rides on his way.

Meantime the Emperor has turned back towards
his own land, and has come to the city of Valtierra, which aforetime Count Roland had taken,
and so destroyed that thenceforward for
the space of a hundred years it was waste
and desolate. There the King awaits
tidings of Ganelon, and the tribute of the great
land of Spain. And now on a morning, at dawn,
with the first light, comes Ganelon into the camp.

*Ganelon
returns to
the Franks*

The Emperor had risen early and heard mass
and matins; and now he is on the green grass
before his tent, and with him is Roland, and
Oliver the valiant, Naymes the Duke and many
another. Thither comes Ganelon, the felon, the
traitor, and with cunning and falsehood speaks to
the King, saying: " Blessed be thou of God! I
bring thee hereby the keys of Saragossa, and great
store of gifts, and twenty hostages — guard thou
them well. But King Marsila bids thee blame
him not that the Caliph be not among them; with
mine own eyes I saw him and four hundred men
of arms, clad in hauberks, with helms on head,
and girt with swords whose hilts were inlaid with
gold, embark together upon the sea. They were
fleeing from Christianity which they would not
receive or hold. But before they had sailed four

leagues, storm and tempest fell upon them, and
even there they were drowned, never shall ye see
them more. Had the Caliph been alive I had
brought him hither. As for the paynim King, in
very truth, lord, this month shall not pass but he
will come to thee in thy kingdom of France, and
will receive the faith that thou holdest, and will
join his hands in thine and become thy man, and
will hold of thee his kingdom of Spain." Then
saith the King: "Thanks be to God therefor.
Well hast thou done, and great shall be Charles
thy reward." Thereafter he let sound a sets forth
for France
thousand trumpets throughout the host, and the
Franks break up their camp, and load their sumpters, and set forth together towards fair France.

Charles the Great has laid waste all Spain, he
has taken its castles and sacked its cities. But
now the war is ended, so saith the King, and he
rides on towards fair France. (The day passes and
evening falls;) Count Roland has set the King's
standard on the crest of a hill against the sky;
and the Franks pitch their tents in all the country
round about. Meantime the paynims ride on
through the valleys, clad in their hauberks and
two-fold harness, helms on head, and girt with
their swords, shields on shoulder, and lances in
hand. They made stay in a wood, on the top of
the mountains, and there four hundred thousand
await the dawn. God, what sorrow the Franks
know it not.

The day fades and night darkens; and Charles, the great Emperor, sleeps. He dreamed that he was come to the great pass of Cizre, and it seemed to him that he held the oaken shaft of his lance in his hand, but Ganelon the Count snatched it from him, brandished and broke it, that its pieces flew towards heaven. But still Charles sleeps and does not waken.

Of the King's dreams

Thereafter he dreamed another dream; that he was before his chapel at Aix and a bear bit him in his arm right cruelly; and anon, from towards Ardennes, he saw come a leopard which fiercely assaulted him ; but even then, from within the hall, a greyhound sprang out, and ran leaping to Charles; first he snapped off the right ear of the bear, then wrathfully he set upon the leopard; and the Franks cried that it was a great battle. Yet none knew which of the twain should conquer. But Charles still sleeps and doth not waken.

Night passes and the clear dawn shines forth, proudly the Emperor gets to horse, and lets sound the trumpets aloud throughout the host. "Lords, barons," then saith Charles, "nigh at hand is the pass and the strait defiles, now choose ye who shall be in the rearguard." And Ganelon answered: "Let it be Roland, my stepson, thou hast no baron so brave as he." Now when the King hears him, he looks at him haughtily, saying: "Thou art a very

Roland chosen captain of the rearguard

devil; and a mortal anger has entered into thee. And who shall go before me in the vanguard?" And Ganelon answered: "Let it be Ogier of Denmark, no baron hast thou more apt thereto."

When Count Roland hears that he is chosen, he speaks out in knightly wise, saying: "Sir kinsman, I should hold thee right dear in that thou hast adjudged the rearguard to me; and by my faith, Charles the King shall lose naught thereby, neither palfrey nor war-horse, nor any he-mule or she-mule whereon man may ride, nay, not so much as a pack-horse or sumpter, an it be not first well paid for by the sword." "Yea, thou speakest truly," saith Ganelon, "that I know well."

— When Count Roland hears that he is to be in the rearguard, wrathfully he turns to his step-father, saying: "Ha, coward and ill son of an ill race, thinkest thou that the glove shall fall from my hand even as did the staff from thine before Charles?" —

(And Count Roland turns to Charles, saying:) "Give me now the bow that you bear in your hand; verily, you shall have no need to chide me that I let it fall, as did Ganelon your right glove when you gave him the herald's staff." But still the Emperor sits with bent head; he plucks at his beard and strokes his moustache, and he may not help but weep.

Thereafter Naymes came before him, a better

vassal was not in all the court, and he spoke to the King, saying: "Well hast thou heard, Count Roland is all in wrath; but the rearguard is adjudged to him, and thou hast no baron who would dare supplant him therein. Give him therefore the bow that you hold, and take heed that he hath good aid." The King holds out the bow and Roland receives it.

And the Emperor speaks to Roland, saying: "Fair sir nephew, know for sooth that I will give over unto thee the half of my army, keep them with thee that they may be thy safeguard." "Nay, not so will I," saith the Count. "May God confound me if I belie my house. J will keep with me twenty thousand Franks of good valour; and do thou cross the mountains in all surety, for so long as I live thou needst fear no man."

Count Roland has mounted his horse; and Oliver his comrade came to stand over against him, and thither came Gerier, and Oton, and Berengier, and thereto came Samson, and Anseïs (the Proud, Ivon and Ivory whom the King holds full dear;) and after them came Gerard the Old of Rousillon, and thereto Engelier the Gascon. Then said the Archbishop: "By my head, I too will go." "And I with thee," quoth Count Gualter, "I am Roland's man and to follow him is my devoir." Then among them they choose out twenty thousand knights.

The Twelve Peers abide in Spain

Thereafter Count Roland calls Gualter del

Hum, saying: "Take thou one thousand Franks of our land of France, and hold the hills and defiles that the Emperor may lose none of his own." "It is my part to do this for thee," saith Gualter. And with a thousand Franks of France he ranges through the hills and passes, nor will he leave the heights for any ill tidings before seven hundred swords have been drawn. Now the same day King Almaris of the kingdom of Belferne shall do him and his men fierce battle.

High are the hills and dark the valleys, brown are the rocks and dread the defiles. That same day the main host of the Franks pass with toil and travail, and fifteen leagues away men might hear the noise of their march. But when that they draw near to the Great Land, and see Gascony, their lord's domain, they call to mind their own fiefs and havings, their young maidens and gentle wives, till there is not one that does not weep for pity. More than all the rest is Charles heavy of heart, in that he has left his nephew in the passes of Spain; pity takes him, and he cannot help but weep.

The Twelve Peers abide in Spain, and in their fellowship are twenty thousand Franks who know not fear or any dread of death. But the Emperor as he draws near to France, hides his face in his mantle. Beside him rides Duke Naymes and he speaks to the King, saying: "Why makest thou such sorrow?" "Ye

Charles feareth for Roland

do ill to ask it," Charles answers him; "such grief is mine I cannot help but make lament. I fear lest through Ganelon France shall be destroyed. This past night, by means of an angel, a dream came to me, and it seemed to me that Ganelon shattered to bits the lance I held in my hand; and he it was who adjudged the rearguard to Roland. And now him I have left behind in a strange land. God, if I lose him never shall I find his fellow."

Charles the Great cannot help but weep; and a hundred thousand Franks are full of pity for him, and a marvellous fear for Roland. Ganelon the felon has done this treason; and rich are the gifts he has received therefor from the paynim king, gold and silver, silks and ciclatons, mules and horses, and camels and lions. Meantime King Marsila calls together the barons of Spain, counts, and viscounts, dukes, and almaçurs, and emirs, and sons of counts; four hundred thousand has he gathered together in three days. He lets sound his tabours throughout Saragossa; and on the topmost tower the paynims raise an image of Mahound, and there is not a man but offers prayers to it and worships it. Thereafter they ride through the land of Cerdagne, over hill and through dale, each seeking to outdo other, till they see the gonfanons of the men of France, the rearguard of the Twelve Peers; they will not fail to do them battle.

Among the foremost comes the nephew of Marsila, riding a mule the which he urges on with a staff; frank and free he saith to his uncle: "Fair Sir King, well have I served thee and much travail and hardship has been mine thereby; for thee have I done battle many a time and for thee have I conquered, and now in return I would fain have a gift — the death blow of Roland. Slay him I will with the point of my lance, an Mahound will help me; and thereby will I set free all the parts of Spain, from the passes of Aspre even unto Durestant. Charles will grow weary, and his Franks will yield them; and thou shalt have peace all the days of thy life." And in answer King Marsila gives him his glove.

Ælroth craves a boon

Holding the glove in his hand, the nephew of Marsila speaks to his uncle right proudly, saying: "Fair Sir King, this is a goodly gift thou hast given me. Now choose for me eleven of thy barons, that I may do battle with the Twelve Peers." The first to answer him was Falseron, the brother of King Marsila: "Fair sir nephew, I will go with thee; together, in good sooth, we will do this battle; and for the rearguard of the great army of Charles, certes, we shall slay them."

Then forth stands King Corsablis, he is of Barbary and a man of wiles; and now he speaks out like a knight of good courage, for not for all God's gold would he do cowardly. And behold Malprimis de Brigal comes hasting up, swifter than horse can gallop he speeds on foot, and before Marsila he cries in a loud voice: "I will go into Roncevals, and if I find Roland I will slay him with my own hand."

An Emir there is of Balaguer, well-fashioned is he of body, and fair and proud of face; and mounted on his horse he rejoices in the bearing of arms; well famed is he for his courage, and had he but Christianity he were a goodly baron. He now comes before Marsila and cries: "I would go into Roncevals, and if I find Roland he shall die the death, and thereto shall Oliver and all the Twelve Peers, and the Franks shall die in dolour and shame. Charles the Great is old and in his dotage, he will weary of waging strong war upon us, and Spain shall rest in peace." And therefor King Marsila gives him good thanks.

The calling of the Twelve Peers of Paynimry

Among the paynims is an Almaçur of Moriane, there is none more fell in all the land of Spain. He likewise has made his boast before Marsila: "Into Roncevals I will lead my men, to the number of twenty thousand, all armed with shields and lances. And if I find Roland I pledge me to slay him, never will the day dawn when Charles shall not lament him."

Then stands forth Turgis of Tortosa, Count he is, and lord of the aforesaid city, and he would slay the Christians with a great slaughter. Beside the others he takes his place before Marsila, saying to the King: "Be not afraid. Mahound is mightier than Saint Peter of Rome, serve ye him and ye shall have victory in the field; at Roncevals I will seek out Roland, and no man shall save him from death. Lo, here is my sword, long it is and goodly, and I will measure it against Durendal, and ye shall hear which of the twain avails most in the fight. The Franks shall die or yield them to us, and thereby shall Charles the Old be brought to dolour and shame; nevermore shall he wear crown on head."

Hard by is Escremis of Valtierra, a Saracen is he, and lord of that land; and now from amid the press about Marsila he cries: "I will go into Roncevals and bring to naught the proud; if I find Roland he shall not bear thence his head, nor shall Oliver the captain; and for the Twelve Peers, they are doomed; the Franks shall perish, and France shall be made desolate, and of goodly vassals Charles shall be despoiled."

Hard by is a paynim hight Esturgant, and with him is Estramaris, his comrade, felons both and misbelieving traitors. Them Marsila called, saying: "Come hither, lords, I would that ye twain go into the passes of Roncevals, and there help to array my folk." And they make him answer, saying: "Lord, even as thou commandest so will we do. And we will set upon Roland and Oliver, and the Twelve Peers shall have no surety from death, for our swords

They swear the death of Roland

are sharp and goodly, and we will smite till they be all red with the warm blood. The Franks shall die, and Charles shall be sore stricken. And as a gift we will give thee the Great Land; come thither, lord, and thou shalt see these things in very sooth; yea, and the Emperor himself we will give over unto thee."

Now thither comes hasting Magaris of Sibilie, he who holds all the land down to the sea. Well loved is he of ladies by reason of his fairness, and no woman can set eyes upon him but her face brightens, and will she, nill she, she must laugh for very joy of him. And of his prowess he has no fellow among the paynims. He now presses through the throng, crying above all the rest to the King: "Be ye no whit adread. I will go into Roncevals and there slay Roland, nor shall Oliver go thence a living man, and the Twelve Peers abide there but for their death. Lo, here is my sword hilted with gold; the Amiral of Primes it was gave it me, and I pledge my faith it shall seek and find the red blood. The Franks shall perish and France be brought to shame. Never shall the day dawn when Charles the Old of the white beard shall not suffer dolour and wrath thereby. Within the year we shall have taken France, and thou mayst lie in the burg of Saint Denis." And at his words the paynim King bows low.

Hard by is Chernuble of the Black Valley.

His long hair falls even unto the ground; and in jest, for his disport, he can bear a greater burden than can be laid upon seven mules. The land (wherein he dwells filleth men with fear;) there the sun doth not shine nor can the corn ripen, no rain falls, neither does the dew gather upon the earth; all black are the rocks of that land, and some say it is the abode of devils. And now Chernuble speaks, saying: "I have girt on my good sword, and at Roncevals I will dye it red; if on my path I meet with Roland the valiant, never believe me more if I do not set upon him in battle, and with my own sword I will conquer Durendal. The Franks shall perish, and France shall be destroyed." And when he had spoken the Twelve Peers gathered together, and with them went a hundred thousand Saracens; keen and eager for battle were they all, and in a fir wood, hard by, they did on their harness.

The paynims arm themselves with Saracen hauberks, of which the more part are of three-fold thickness; they lace on helms of right good Saracen work, and gird on swords of Viennese steel, fair are their shields, and their lances are of Valencia, tipped with gonfanons white and blue and scarlet. They leave behind them the mules and palfries, and mounting their war-horses, ride forth in close ranks. Fair was the day and bright the sun, and all their harness glistens in the light. And

The horns of the Saracens

for the more joy they let sound a thousand trumpets; so great is the noise thereof that the Franks hear it. Then saith Oliver: "Sir comrade, methinks we shall have ado with the Saracens." "Now God grant it be as thou sayest," Roland answers him, "for to make stand here for our King is to do as good men ought to do. Verily for his liege a man well ought to suffer pain and woe, and endure both great heat and great cold, and should hold him ready to lose both hide and hair in his lord's service. Now let each have a care that he strikes good blows and great, that no man may mis-say us in his songs. These misbelieving men are in the wrong, and right is with the Christians, and for my part I will give ye no ill example."

"THE AMIRAL TAKETH COUNSEL WITH THE KINGS"

"THEY LET SOUND A THOUSAND TRUMPETS"

PART II

THE BATTLE AT RONCEVALS

THEN Oliver goes up into a high mountain,
and looks away to the right, all down a grassy
valley, and sees the host of the heathen
coming on, and he called to Roland, his
comrade, saying: "From the side of
Spain I see a great light coming, thousands of
white hauberks and thousands of gleaming helms.
They will fall upon our Franks with great wrath.
Ganelon the felon has done this treason, and he
it was adjudged us to the rearguard, before the
Emperor." "Peace Oliver," saith Count Roland, "he is my mother's husband, speak thou
no ill of him."

Oliver has fared up the mountain, and from
the summit thereof he sees all the kingdom of
Spain and the great host of the Saracens. Wondrous is the shine of helmets studded with gold,
of shields and broidered hauberks, of lances and
gonfanons. The battles are without number,
and no man may give count thereof, so great is
the multitude. Oliver was all astonied at the
sight; he got him down the hill as best he might,

and came to the Franks, and gave them his tidings.

"I have seen the paynims," said Oliver; "never was so great a multitude seen of living men. Those of the vanguard are upon a hundred thousand, all armed with shields and helmets, and clad in white hauberks; right straight are the shafts of their lances, and bright the points thereof. Such a battle we shall have as was never before seen of man. Ye lords of France, may God give you might! and stand ye firm that we be not overcome. "Foul fall him who flees!" then say the Franks, "for no peril of death will we fail thee."

"Great is the host of the heathen," saith Oliver, "and few is our fellowship. Roland, fair comrade, I pray thee sound thy horn of ivory that Charles may hear it and return again with all his host." "That were but folly," quoth Roland, "and thereby would I lose all fame in sweet France. Rather will I strike good blows and great with Durendal, that the blade thereof shall be blooded even unto the hilt. Woe worth the paynims that they came into the passes! I pledge thee my faith short life shall be theirs."

Oliver prays Roland to sound his horn

"Roland, comrade, blow now thy horn of ivory, and Charles shall hear it, and bring hither his army again, and the King and his barons shall succour us." But Roland answers him, saying: "Now God forfend that through me my kinsman

be brought to shame, or aught of dishonour befall
fair France. But first I will lay on with Durendal, the good sword that is girded here at my side,
and thou shalt see the blade thereof all reddened.
Woe worth the paynims when they gathered their
hosts! I pledge me they shall all be given over
to death."

"Roland, comrade, blow thy horn of ivory,
that Charles may hear it as he passes the mountains, and I pledge me the Franks will
return hither again." But Roland saith: The pride of Roland
"Now God forfend it be said of any living man
that I sounded my horn for dread of paynims.
Nay, that reproach shall never fall upon my
kindred. But when I am in the stour I will
smite seven hundred blows, or mayhap a thousand, and thou shalt see the blade of Durendal
all crimson. The Franks are goodly men, and
they will lay on right valiantly, nor shall those
of Spain have any surety from death."

Saith Oliver, "I see no shame herein. I have
seen the Saracens of Spain, they cover the hills
and the valleys, the heaths and the plains. Great
are the hosts of this hostile folk, and ours is but
a little fellowship." And Roland makes answer:
"My desire is the greater thereby. May God
and His most holy angels forfend that France
should lose aught of worship through me. Liefer
had I die than bring dishonour upon me. The
Emperor loves us for dealing stout blows."

Roland is brave, and Oliver is wise, and both are good men of their hands; once armed and a-horseback, rather would they die than flee the battle. Hardy are the Counts and high their speech. The felon paynims ride on in great wrath. Saith Oliver: "Roland, prithee look. They are close upon us, but Charles is afar off. Thou wouldst not deign to sound thy horn of ivory; but were the King here we should suffer no hurt. Look up towards the passes of Aspre and thou shalt see the woeful rearguard; they who are of it will do no more service henceforth." But Roland answers him: "Speak not so cowardly. Cursed be the heart that turns coward in the breast! Hold we the field, and ours be the buffets and the slaughter."

When Roland sees that the battle is close upon them he waxes fiercer than lion or leopard. He

Roland is fain for battle

calls to the Franks, and he saith to Oliver: "Comrade, friend, say not so. When the Emperor left us his Franks he set apart such a twenty thousand of men that, certes, among them is no coward. For his liege lord a man ought to suffer all hardship, and endure great heat and great cold, and give both his blood and his body. Lay on with thy lance, and I will smite with Durendal, my good sword that the King gave me. If I die here, may he to whom it shall fall, say, 'This was the sword of goodly vassal.'"

Nigh at hand is Archbishop Turpin; he now

spurs his horse to the crest of a knoll, and speaks
to the Franks, and this is his sermon: "Lords,
barons, Charles left us here, and it
is a man's devoir to die for his King. The Arch-bishop's sermon
Now help ye to uphold Christianity.
Certes, ye shall have a battle, for here before
you are the Saracens. Confess your sins and
pray God's mercy, and that your souls may be
saved I will absolve you. If ye are slain ye
will be holy martyrs, and ye shall have seats in
the higher Paradise." The Franks light off their
horses and kneel down, and the Archbishop blesses
them, and for a penance bids them that they lay
on with their swords.

The Franks get upon their feet, freed and absolved from sin; and the Archbishop blesses them
in the name of God. Then they mounted their
swift horses, and armed themselves after the manner of knights, and made them ready for battle.
Count Roland calls to Oliver, saying: "Sir comrade, rightly thou saidst Ganelon hath betrayed
us all, and hath received gold and silver and goods
therefor; but the Emperor will well revenge us.
King Marsila hath bought and sold us, but he
shall pay for it with the sword."

Roland rides through the passes of Spain on
Veillantif, his good horse and swift. He is clad
in his harness, right well it becomes him, and as
he rides he brandishes his spear, turning its point
towards heaven; and to its top is bound a gon-

fanon of pure white, whereof the golden fringes
fall down even unto his hands. Well fashioned
is his body, and his face fair and laughing; close
behind him rides his comrade; and all the Franks
claim him as their champion. Full haughtily he
looks on the Saracens, but gently and mildly on
the Franks, and he speaks to them courteously,
saying: "Lords, barons, ride on softly. The paynims come seeking destruction, and this day we
shall have plunder so goodly and great that no
King of France hath ever taken any of so great
price." At these words the two hosts come together.

Saith Oliver: "I have no mind for more words.
Thou wouldst not deign to sound thy horn of ivory,
and no help shalt thou get from Charles, naught
he knows of our case, nor is the wrong
his, the baron. They who are beyond
the mountains are no wise to blame.
Now ride on with what might ye may. Lords,
barons, hold ye the field! And in God's name I
pray you bethink you both how to deal good blows
and how to take them. And let us not forget
the device of our King." At these words all the
Franks cried out together, and whosoever may
have heard that cry of Montjoy must call to mind
valour and worth. Then they rode forward,
God! how proudly, spurring their horses for the
more speed, and fell a-smiting — how else should
they do? But no whit adread were the Saracens.

*Franks and
paynims join
battle*

And lo you, Franks and paynims come together in battle.

The nephew of Marsila, who was called Ælroth, rides before all his host, and foul are his words to our Franks: "Ye Frankish felons, today ye shall do battle with us. He who should have been your surety has betrayed you; mad is the King who left you behind in the passes. Today shall fair France lose her fame, and the right arm of Charles shall be smitten off from his body." When Roland hears this, God! how great is his wrath. He spurs as fast as his horse may run, and with all the might he hath he smites Ælroth, and breaks his shield, and rends apart his hauberk, that he cleaves his breast *The Franks win the first blow* and breaks the bone, and severs the spine from the back; with his lance he drives out the soul from the body, for so fierce is the blow Ælroth wavers, and with all the force of his lance Roland hurls him from his horse dead, his neck broken in two parts. Yet Roland still chides him, saying: "Out coward! Charles is not mad, nor loves he treason. He did well and knightly to leave us in the passes. Today shall France lose naught of her fame. Franks, lay on! Ours is the first blow. Right is with us, and these swine are in the wrong."

Among the paynims is a Duke, Falsaron by name, who was brother to King Marsila, and held the land of Dathan and Abiram; there is no more shameless felon on all the earth; so wide is his forehead that the space between his eyes measures a full half foot. When he sees his nephew slain, he is full of dole, and he drives through the press as swift as he may, and cries aloud the paynim war-cry. Great is his hatred of the Franks. "Today shall fair France lose her fame!" Oliver hears him and is passing wroth; with his golden spurs he pricks on his horse and rides upon him like a true baron; he breaks the shield, tears asunder the hauberk, and drives his lance into the body up to the flaps of his pennon, and with the might of his blow hurls him dead from the saddle. He looks to earth where lies the felon, and speaks him haughtily: "Coward, naught care I for thy threats. Lay on Franks, certes, we shall overcome them." And he cries out Montjoy, the war-cry of Charles.

A King there is, Corsablis by name; he is of Barbary, a far-off land, and he spoke to the Saracens, saying: "We shall win a fair day on these Franks for few is their fellowship. And such as be here shall prove themselves of small avail, nor shall one be saved alive for Charles; the day has come whereon they must die." Archbishop Turpin hears him right well, and to no man under heaven has he ever borne such hate; with his spurs of fine gold he pricks on his horse, and rides upon the King with great might, cleaves his shield and rends his hauberk, and thrusts his great lance

into his body, and so drives home the blow that
sorely the King wavers, and with all the force of
his lance Turpin hurls him dead into the path.
He looks on the ground where he sees the glut-
ton lie, nor doth he withhold him from speech,
but saith: "Coward and heathen, thou hast lied!
Charles, my liege lord, is ever our
surety, and our Franks have no mind
to flee; and we shall have a care that
thy comrades go not far hence; yea, and a second death must ye suffer. Lay on ye Franks, let
no man forget himself! This first blow is ours,
thanks be to God." And he cries out Montjoy,
to hold the field.

The slaying of the paynim peers

And Gerin smites Malprimis de Brigal, that
his good shield no whit avails him, he shatters
the jewelled boss thereof, and half of it falls to
earth, he pierces the hauberk to the flesh, and
drives his good lance into the body; the paynim
falls down in a heap, and his soul is carried away
by Satan.

And Gerier, the comrade of Gerin, smites the
Emir, and shatters his shield and unmails his
hauberk, and thrusts his good lance into his heart;
so great is the blow his lance drives through the
body, and with all the force of his shaft he throws
him to the ground dead. "Ours is a goodly battle," quoth Oliver.

Samson the Duke rides upon the Almaçur, and
breaks his shield all flowered and set with gold,

nor doth his good hauberk give him any surety,
but Samson pierces him through heart and liver
and lungs, and fells him dead, whether any one
grieves for him or no. Saith the Archbishop:
"That was knightly stricken."

And Anseïs urges on his horse and encounters with Turgis of Tortosa, cleaves his shield
below the golden boss, rends asunder his twofold
hauberk, and sets the point of his good lance
in his body, and thrusts so well that the iron
passes sheer through him, that the might of the
blow hurls him to the ground dead. "That was
the buffet of a man of good prowess," saith Roland.

And Engelier, the Gascon of Bordeaux, spurs
his horse, slackens his rein, and encounters with
Escremis of Valtierra, breaks and carves the shield
from his shoulder, rends apart the ventail of his
hauberk, and smites him in his breast between
his two collar bones, and with the might of the
blow hurls him from the saddle, saying: "Ye are
all given over to destruction."

And Oton smites the paynim Esturgant upon
the leathern front of his shield, marring all the
blue and white thereof, breaks through the sides
of his hauberk, and drives his good spear and
sharp into his body, and casts him from his swift
horse, dead. "Naught may save thee," saith
Oliver thereat.

And Berengier rides on Estramaris, shatters

his shield, rends asunder his hauberk, and drives his stout lance into his body, and smites him dead amid a thousand Saracens. Of the Twelve Peers ten are now slain and but two are still living men, to wit, Chernuble and Count Margaris.

Margaris is a right valiant knight, strong and goodly, swift and keen; he spurs his horse and rides on Oliver, breaks his shield below the boss of pure gold, that the lance past along his side, but by God's help, it did not pierce the body; the shaft grazes him but doth not overthrow him, and Margaris drives on, in that he has no hindrance, and sounds his horn to call his men about him.

Now the battle waxes passing great on both parties. Count Roland spares himself no whit, but smites with his lance as long as the shaft holds, but by fifteen blows it is broken and lost; thereupon he draws out Durendal his good sword, all naked, spurs his horse and rides on Chernuble, breaks his helm whereon the carbuncles blaze, cleaves his mail-coif and the hair of his head that the sword cuts through eyes and face, and the white hauberk of fine mail, and all the body to the fork of the legs, sheer into the saddle of beaten gold, nor did the sword stint till it had entered the horse and cleft the backbone, never staying for joint, that man and horse fell dead upon the thick grass. Thereupon Roland cried: "Coward, woe worth the day thou camest hither! no help shalt thou get from Mahound; nor by such swine as thou shall today's battle be achieved."

Count Roland rides through the press; in his hand he hath Durendal, right good for hacking and hewing, and doth great damage upon the Saracens. Lo, how he hurls one dead upon another, and the bright blood flows out on the field. All reddened are his hauberk and his arms, and the neck and shoulders of his good horse. Nor doth Oliver hold back from the battle; the Twelve Peers do not shame themselves, and all the Franks smite and slay, that the paynims perish or fall swooning. Then saith the Archbishop, "Our barons do passing well," and he cries out Montjoy, the war-cry of Charles.

The Franks do passing well

Oliver drives through the stour; his lance is broken and naught is left him but the truncheon; yet he smites the paynim Malsaron that his shield patterned with gold and flowers is broken, and his two eyes fly out from his head, and his brains fall at his feet; among seven hundred of his fellows Oliver smites him dead. Then he slew Turgin and Esturgus, and thereby broke his lance that it splintered even unto the pommel. Thereat Roland saith: "Comrade what dost thou? I have no mind for a staff in so great battle, rather a man hath need of iron and steel. Where is thy sword Halteclere?" "I may not draw it," Oliver answered him. "So keen am I to smite."

But now the lord Oliver hath drawn his good sword, even as his comrade had besought him, and hath shown it to him in knightly wise; and therewith he smites the paynim Justin de Val Ferrée that he severs his head in twain, cuts through his broidered hauberk and his body, through his good saddle set with gold, and severs the backbone of his steed, that man and horse fall dead on the field before him. Then said Roland: "Now I hold you as my brother, and 't is for such buffets the Emperor loves us." And on all sides they cry out Montjoy.

Count Gerin rides his horse Sorel, and Gerier, his comrade, rides Passecerf; both slacken rein, and spurring mightly set upon the paynim Timosel; one smites him on the shield, and the other on the hauberk, that both their lances break in his body; and he falls dead in the field. I wot not, nor have I ever heard man say, which of the twain was the more swift. Then Esperveris, son of Borel, died at the hand of Engelier of Bordeaux. And the Archbishop slew Siglorel, that enchanter who of old had passed down into hell, led thither by the spells of Jupiter. "Of him we are well rid," quoth Turpin. And Roland answered him: "Yea, the coward is overthrown. Oliver, my brother, such buffets please me right well."

Meantime the battle waxes passing hard, and both Franks and paynims deal such blows that it is wonder to see; here they smite, and there make what defence they may; and many a lance is The battle waxes hard broken and reddened, and there is great rending of pennons and ensigns. Many a good Frank loses his youth, and will never again see wife or mother, or the men of France who await him in the passes. Charles the Great weeps for them, and makes great sorrow; but what avails it? no help shall they get therefrom. An ill turn Ganelon did them the day he sold his own kindred in Saragossa. Thereafter he lost both life and limb therefor; in the council at Aix, he was condemned to hang, and with him upon thirty of his kindred to whom death left no hope.

Dread and sore is the battle. Roland and Oliver lay on valiantly, and the Archbishop deals more than a thousand buffets, nor are the Twelve Peers backward, and all the Franks smite as a man. The paynims are slain by hundreds and thousands, whosoever does not flee has no surety from death, but will he, nill he, must take his end. But the Franks lose their goodliest arms; [lances adorned with gold, and trenchant spears, and gonfanons red and white and blue, and the blades of their good swords are broken, and thereto they lose many a valiant knight.] Never again shall they see father or kindred, or Charles their liege lord who abides for them in the passes.

Meantime, in France, a wondrous tempest broke forth, a mighty storm of wind and lightning, with rain and hail out of all measure, and bolts of thunder that fell ever and again; and verily therewith came a quaking of the earth that ran through all the land from A wondrous tempest Saint Michael of the Peril, even unto *Xanten*, and from Besançon to the port of Guitsand; and there was not a dwelling whose walls were not rent asunder. And at noon fell a shadow of great darkness, nor was there any light save as the heavens opened. They that saw these things were sore afraid, and many a one said: "This is the day of judgment and the end of the world is at hand." But they were deceived, and knew not whereof they spoke; it was the great mourning for the death of Roland.

Meantime the Franks smote manfully and with good courage, and the paynims were slain by thousands and by multitudes; of a hundred thousand not two may survive. Then said the Archbishop: "Our Franks are of good prowess, no man under heaven Of all the paynims only Margaris escapes the battle hath better, it is written in the annals of France that valiant they are for our Emperor." And the Franks fare through the field seeking their fellows, and weeping from dole and pity for their kin, in all love and kindness. But even now King Marsila is upon them with his great host.

[Count Roland is a knight of much worship, so likewise are Oliver and the Twelve Peers, and all the Franks are good warriors. By their great might they have made such slaughter of paynims that of a hundred thousand, only one hath escaped, Margaris to wit. Blame him not that he fled, for in his body he bore the wounds of four lances. Back he fared in haste towards Spain, and came to Marsila and gave him tidings. . . . And in a loud voice he cried: "Good King of Spain, now ride on with all speed, the Franks are weary and spent with the smiting and slaying of our Saracens; they have lost their lances and spears, and a good half of their men, and those who yet live are weakened, and the more part of them maimed and bleeding, nor have they more arms wherewith to help themselves.]

Marsila comes on down the valley with the mighty host that he has assembled; full twenty battles the King has arrayed. There is a great shining of helmets, set with gold and precious stones, and of shields and of broidered *The second paynim host* hauberks. Trumpets to the number of seven thousand sound the onset, and the din thereof runs far and wide. Then saith Roland: "Oliver, comrade and brother, Ganelon the felon has sworn our death. The treason is manifest, and great vengeance shall the Emperor take therefor. The battle will be sore and great, such a one as was never before fought of man. I will smite with Durendal my sword, and do thou, comrade, lay on with Halteclere. Through many lands have we carried them, and with them have we

conquered many a battle , no ill song must be sung
of them."

When the Franks see how great is the multitude
of the paynims, that on all sides they cover the
field, they call upon Roland, and Oliver, and the
Twelve Peers, that they be their defence. Then
the Archbishop tells them his mind, saying:
"Lords, barons, put from you all cowardly
thoughts; and in God's name I pray you give
not back. Better it were that we die in battle
than that men of worship should speak foully of
us in their songs. Certain it is we shall straightway take our end, nor shall we from today be
living men; yet there is a thing I can promise
ye, blessed paradise shall be opened to you, and
ye shall take your place among the innocent." At
his words, the Franks take heart, and every man
cries out Montjoy.

[Wily and cunning is King Marsila, and he
saith to the paynims: "Now set your trust in me;
this Roland is of wondrous might, and he who
would overcome him must strive his uttermost;
in two encounters he will not be vanquished methinks, and if not, we will give him three. Then
Charles the King shall lose his glory, and shall see
France fall into dishonour. Ten battles Grandonie
shall abide here with me, and the remain- leads the
ing ten shall set upon the Franks." Then second
battle
to Grandonie he gave a broidered banner that it
might be a sign unto the rest, and gave over to
him the commandment.

King Marsila abides on the mountain, and Grandonie comes on down the valley. By three golden nails he has made fast his gonfanon; and he cries aloud: "Now ride on, ye barons!" And for the more goodly noise he bids them sound a thousand trumpets. Say the Franks: "God our Father, what shall we do? Woe worth the day we saw Count Ganelon! he hath sold us by foul treason. Now help us, ye Twelve Peers!" But the first to answer them is the Archbishop, saying: "Good knights, this day great honour shall be yours, for God will give you crowns and flowers in Paradise among the glorious; but therein the coward shall not enter." And the Franks make answer: "We will lay on as one man, and though we die we will not betray him." Then they spur on with their golden spurs to smite the miscreant felons.]

Among the paynims is a Saracen of Saragossa, lord he is of half the city, and Climborin, he hight; never will he flee from any living man. He it was who swore fellowship with Count Ganelon, kissed him in all friendship upon the lips, and gave him his helm and his carbuncle. And he Engelier is hath sworn to bring the Great Land to slain shame, and to strip the Emperor of his crown. He rides his horse whom he calls Bar-bamusche, that is swifter than falcon or swallow; and slackening his rein, he spurs mightily, and rides upon Engelier of Gascony that neither shield

nor byrnie may save him, but he drives the head
of his lance into his body, thrusting so manfully
that the point thereof passes through to the other
side, and with all the might of his lance hurls him
in the field dead. Thereafter he cries: "These
folk are good to slay!" But the Franks say:
"Alack, that so good a knight should take his
end."

And Count Roland speaks to Oliver, saying:
"Sir comrade, now is Engelier slain, nor have we
any knight of more valour." And the Count
answers him, saying: "Now God grant me to
avenge him." He pricks on his horse with spurs
of pure gold, and he grasps Halteclere — already
is the blade thereof reddened — and with all his
strength he smites the paynim; he drives the blow
home that the Saracen falls; and the devils carry
away his soul. Then Oliver slew Duke Alphaïen,
and cut off the head of Escababi, and unhorsed
seven Arabs, — never again shall they do battle.
Then said Roland: "Wroth is my comrade, and
now at my side he wins great worship; for such
blows Charles holds us the more dear." And he
cried aloud: "To battle, knights, to battle!"

Hard by is the paynim Valdabrun, that had
stood godfather to King Marsila; on the sea he
is lord of four hundred dromonds, and
well honoured of all shipmen. He it
was who aforetime took Jerusalem by
treason, violated the temple of Solomon, and

*Roland
avenges
Samson*

slew the patriarch before the baptismal fonts. And he had sworn fellowship with Ganelon, and had given him a sword and a thousand mangons. He rides a horse called Gramimond, swifter than any falcon; he spurs him well with his sharp spurs, and rides upon Samson the mighty Duke, breaks his shield, and rends his hauberk, and drives the flaps of his gonfanon into his body, and with all the force of his lance hurls him from the saddle dead. "Lay on, paynims, for hardily we shall overthrow them!" But the Franks cry: "God, woe worth the good baron!"

When Roland sees that Samson is dead, ye may guess he is sore stricken, he spurs his horse and lets him run as fast as he may, in his hand he holds Durendal, of greater worth than is pure gold, and with all the might he hath, he smites the paynim on the helm set with gold and gems, and cuts through head and hauberk and body, and through the good saddle set with gold and jewels, deep into the back of the horse, and slays both him and his rider, whosoever has dole or joy thereof. Cry the paynims: "That was a woeful blow for us." Then quoth Roland: "No love have I for any one of ye, for yours is the pride and the iniquity."

Among the paynims is an African, Malquiant, son of King Malcud; his armour is all of the beaten gold, and brighter than all the rest it shines to heaven. His horse, which he calls Salt-Perdut, is so swift that he has not his fellow in any four-footed beast. And now Malquiant rode on Anseïs, and smote him full on the shield that its scarlet and blue were hewn away, and he rent the sides of his hauberk, and drave his lance into his body, both point and shaft. Dead is the Count and done are his life days. Thereat cry the Franks: "Alack for thee, good baron!"

Through the press rides Turpin the Archbishop — never did another priest say mass who did with his own strength so great deeds of arms — and he saith to the paynim: "Now may God bring all evil upon thee! for thou hast slain one for whom my heart is sore stricken." Then he set his good horse at a gallop, and smote Malquiant on his shield of Toledo, that he fell dead upon the green grass.

Turpin slays Malquiant

Hard by is the paynim Grandonie, son of Capuel, King of Cappadocia; he rides a horse called Marmorie, swifter than any bird that flies; he now slackens rein, and spurring well, thrusts mightily upon Gerin, breaks his crimson shield that it falls from his shoulder, and rends all asunder his hauberk, and thereafter drives all his blue gonfanon into his body that he falls dead beside a great rock. Then he slays Gerier, Gerin's comrade, and Berengier, and Guyon of Saint-Antonie; and thereafter he smote Austor, the mighty Duke that held Valence and the land along the Rhône, and felled him dead that the paynims had great joy thereof. But the Franks cry: "How many of ours are stricken."

Roland holds his ruddied sword in his hand; he has heard the Franks make lament, and so great is his sorrow that his heart is nigh to bursting, and he saith to the paynims: "Now may God bring all evil upon thee! Methinks thou shalt pay me dear for him thou hast slain." And he spurs his horse, which springs forward eagerly; and let whoso will pay the price, the two knights join battle.

Grandonie was a man of good prowess, of much valour and hardiness, and amid the way he encounters with Roland, and albeit before that time he had never set eyes upon him, he none the less knew him of a certainty by his look and countenance; and he could not but be sore adread at the sight, and fain would he have fled, but he could not. The Count smites him mightily that he rends all his helm down to the nasal, cleaves through nose and mouth and teeth, through the hauberk of fine mail, and all the body, splits the silver sides from off the golden saddle, and cuts deep into the back of the horse, that both he and his rider are slain beyond help. Thereat those of Spain make great lament, but the Franks cry: "That was well stricken of our captain."

Grandonie is smitten down

Wondrous and fierce is the battle; the Franks lay on in their wrath and their might, that hands and sides and bones fall to earth, and garments are rent off to the very flesh, and the blood runs down to the green grass. (The pay-nims cry: "We may not longer endure.) May the curse of Mahound fall upon the Great Land, for its folk have not their fellows for hardiness." And there was not a man but cried out: "Marsila! haste, O King, for we are in sore need of thy help."

Again the paynims give back

Wondrous and great is the battle. And still the Franks smite with their burnished lances. There is great dolour of folk, and many a man is slain and maimed and bleeding, and one lies on another, or on his back, or face down. The Saracens may not longer endure, but howsoever unwillingly they must give back. And eagerly the Franks pursue after them.

Marsila sees the slaughter of his people, and lets sound his horns and bussynes, and gets to horse with all his vassal host. In the foremost front rides the Saracen Abisme, the falsest knight of his fellowship, all compact of evil and villainy. He believes not in God the son of Mary; and he is black as melted pitch. Dearer than all the gold of Galicia he loves treachery and murder, nor did any man ever see him laugh or take disport. But he is a good man of arms, and bold to rashness, wherefor he is well beloved of the felon King Marsila, and to him it is given to bear the Dragon, around

Marsila leads the third battle

which the paynims gather.   The Archbishop hath
small love for Abisme, and so soon as he sees him
he is all desirous to smite him, and quietly, within
himself, he saith: "This Saracen seems a misbelieving felon, I had liefer die than not set upon
him to slay him; never shall I love coward or
cowardice."

Whereupon the Archbishop begins the battle.
He rides the horse that he won from Grossaille, a
King whom he slew in Denmark; the good steed
is swift and keen, featly fashioned of foot, and
flat of leg; short in the thigh and large of croupe,
long of flank and high of back; his tail is white
and yellow his mane, his head is the colour of the
fawn, and small are his ears; of all four-footed
beasts none may outstrip him.   The Archbishop
spurs mightily, and will not fail to meet with
Abisme and smite him on his shield, a very marvel, set with gems, — topaz and amethysts, and
precious crystals, and blazing carbuncles; the gift
it was of Galafré the Amiral, who had received it
of a devil in Val-Metas.   Now Turpin smites it and
spares it not, that after his buffet it has not the
worth of a doit.   And he pierces Abisme through
the body, and hurls him dead in the open field.
And the Franks say: "That was a good deed of
arms; in the hands of our Archbishop safe is the
crosier."

And Count Roland speaks to Oliver, saying:
'Sir comrade, what say ye, is not the Arch·

bishop a right good knight, that there is no better
under heaven? for well he knows how to smite
with lance and spear." "Now let us aid
him," the Count makes answer. And
at these words the Franks go into battle The Franks are sore smitten
again; great are the blows and grievous the
slaughter, and great is the dolour of the Christians.

[The Franks have lost much of their arms, yet
still there are a good four hundred of naked swords
with which they smite and hew on shining helmets. God, how many a head is cleft in twain;
and there is great rending of hauberks and un-
mailing of byrnies; and they smite off feet and
hands and heads. The paynims cry: "These
Franks sore mishandle us, whoso doth not defend
himself hath no care for his life." (King Marsila
hears them make lament, and saith in his wrath):
"Terra Major, now may Mahound destroy thee,
for thy folk hath discomfited mine, and hath
destroyed and spoiled me of many cities which
Charles of the white beard now holds; he hath
conquered Rome and Apulia and Calabria, Constantinople, and Saxony the wide, liefer had I die
than flee before him. Paynims, now lay on that
the Franks may have no surety. If Roland dies,
Charles loses the life of his body; if he lives, we
shall all take our end."

The felon paynims again smite with their lances
upon shields and bright helmets; so great is the

shock of iron and steel that the flame springs out
toward heaven; and lo, how the blood and the
brains run down! Great is the dolour and grief
Roland's   of Roland when he sees so many good
grief   knights take their end; he calls to remembrance the land of France, and his uncle,
Charlemagne the good King, and he cannot help
but be heavy.

Yet still he thrust through the press and did
not leave from smiting. In his hand he held
Durendal, his good sword, and rent hauberks,
and broke helmets, and pierced hands and heads
and trunks that he threw a hundred paynims to
ground, they who had held themselves for good
men of arms.

And on his side the lord Oliver drave forward,
smiting great blows; in his hand he held Halteclere, his good and trusty sword that had not
its fellow under heaven, save only Durendal, and
with it he fought valourously; all stained he was
with blood even to his arms. "God," saith Roland, "that is a goodly baron. O gentle Count,
all courage and all loyalty, this day our friendship
must have an end, for today through great woe
we twain must part. Never again shall we see
the Emperor; never again shall there be such
lamentation in fair France. The Frankish folk
will pray for us, and in holy churches orisons
will be offered; certes, our souls will come into
Paradise." Oliver slackens rein and spurs his

horse, and in the thick of press comes nigh unto
Roland, and one saith unto other: "Comrade,
keep near me; so long as death spares me I will
not fail thee."]

Would ye had seen Roland and Oliver hack
and hew with their swords, and the Archbishop
smite with his lance. We can reckon those that
fell by their hands for the number thereof is written in charter and record; the Geste says more
than four thousand. In four encounters all went
well with the Franks, but the fifth was sore and
grievous to them, for in this all their knights were
slain save only sixty, spared by God's mercy.
Before they die they will sell their lives dear.

When Count Roland is ware of the great
slaughter of his men, he turns to Oliver, saying:
"Sir comrade, as God may save thee,
see how many a good man of arms lies *He would fain blow his horn*
on the ground; we may well have pity
on sweet France, the fair, that must now be desolate of such barons. Ah, King and friend, would
thou wert here! Oliver, my brother, what shall
we do? How shall we send him tidings?" "Nay,
I know not how to seek him," saith Oliver; "but
liefer had I die than bring dishonour upon me."

Then saith Roland: "I will sound my horn of
ivory, and Charles, as he passes the mountains,
will hear it; and I pledge thee my faith the
Franks will return again." Then saith Oliver:
"Therein would be great shame for thee, and dis-

honour for all thy kindred, a reproach that would last all the days of their life. Thou wouldst not sound it when I bid thee, and now thou shalt not by my counsel. And if thou dost sound it, it will not be hardily, for now both thy arms are stained with blood." "Yea," the Count answers him, "I have dealt some goodly blows."

But Oliver chideth him

Then saith Roland: "Sore is our battle, I will blow a blast, and Charles the King will hear it." "That would not be knightly," saith Oliver; "when I bid thee, comrade, thou didst disdain it. Had the King been here, we had not suffered this damage; but they who are afar off are free from all reproach. By this my beard, an I see again my sister, Aude the Fair, never shalt thou lie in her arms."

Then saith Roland: "Wherefore art thou wroth with me?" And Oliver answers him, saying: "Comrade, thou thyself art to blame. Wise courage is not madness, and measure is better than rashness. Through thy folly these Franks have come to their death; nevermore shall Charles the King have service at our hands. Hadst thou taken my counsel, my liege lord had been here, and this battle had been ended, and King Marsila had been or taken or slain. Woe worth thy prowess, Roland! Henceforth Charles shall get no help of thee; never till God's Judgment Day shall there be such another man; but thou must

die, and France shall be shamed thereby. And
this day our loyal fellowship shall have an end;
before this evening grievously shall we be parted."

The Archbishop, hearing them dispute together,
spurs his horse with his spurs of pure gold, and
comes unto them, and rebukes them, saying:
"Sir Roland, and thou, Sir Oliver, in God's
name I pray ye, let be this strife. Little help
shall we now have of thy horn; and yet it were
better to sound it; if the King come, he will
revenge us, and the paynims shall not go hence
rejoicing. Our Franks will light off their horses,
and find us dead and maimed, and they will lay us
on biers, on the backs of sumpters, and will weep
for us with dole and pity; and they will bury us
in the courts of churches, that our bones may not
be eaten by wolves and swine and dogs." "Sir,
thou speakest well and truly," quoth Roland.

And therewith he sets his ivory horn to his lips,
grasps it well and blows it with all the might he
hath. High are the hills, and the sound echoes
far, and for thirty full leagues they hear it resound. Charles and all his host hear it,
and the King saith: "Our men are at   The Franks
                                         hear the
battle." But Count Ganelon denies it,   blast
saying: "Had any other said so, we had deemed
it great falsehood."

With dolour and pain, and in sore torment,
Count Roland blows his horn of ivory, that the
bright blood springs out of his mouth, and the

temples of his brain are broken. Mighty is the blast of the horn, and Charles, passing the mountains, hears it, and Naymes hears it, and all the Franks listen and hear. Then saith the King: "I hear the horn of Roland; never would he sound it, an he were not at battle." But Ganelon answers him, saying: "Battle is there none; thou art old and white and hoary, and thy words are those of a child. Well thou knowest the great pride of Roland; — a marvel it is that God hath suffered it thus long. Aforetime he took Noples against thy commandment, and when the Saracens came out of the city and set upon Roland the good knight, (he slew them with Durendal his sword;) thereafter with water he washed away the blood which stained the meadow, that none might know of what he had done. And for a single hare he will blow his horn all day long; and now he but boasts among his fellows, for there is no folk on earth would dare do him battle. I prithee ride on. Why tarry we? The Great Land still lies far before us."

Count Roland's mouth has burst out a-bleeding, and the temples of his brain are broken. In dolour and pain he sounds his horn of ivory; but Charles hears it and the Franks hear it. Saith the King: "Long drawn is the blast of that horn." "Yea," Naymes answers, "for in sore need is the baron who blows it. Certes, our men are at battle; and he who now dissembles hath betrayed

Roland. Take your arms and cry your war-cry, and succour the men of your house. Dost thou not hear Roland's call?"

The Emperor has commanded that his trumpets be sounded, and now the Franks light down from their horses and arm themselves with hauberks and helms and swords adorned with gold; fair are their shields, Charles turneth back and goodly and great their lances, and their gonfanons are scarlet and white and blue. Then all the barons of the host get them to horse, and spur through the passes; and each saith to other: "An we may but see Roland a living man, we will strike good blows at his side." But what avails it? for they have abode too long.

Clear is the evening as was the day, and all their armour glistens in the sun, and there is great shining of hauberks, and helms, and shields painted with flowers, and lances, and gilded gonfanons. The Emperor rides on in wrath, and the Franks are full of care and foreboding; and not a man but weeps full sore and hath great fear for Roland. Then the King let take Count Ganelon, and gave him over to the cooks of his household; and he called Besgon their chief, saying: "Guard him well, as beseems a felon who hath betrayed my house." Besgon took him, Ganelon a prisoner and set a watch about him of a hundred of his fellows of the kitchen, both best and worst. They plucked out the hairs of Ganelon's beard and moustache, and each one dealt him four blows with his fist, and hardily they beat him with rods and staves; then they put about his neck a chain, and bound him even as they would a bear, and in derision they set him upon a sumpter. So they guard him till they return him unto Charles.

High are the hills and great and dark, deep the valleys, and swift the waters. To answer Roland's horn all the trumpets are sounded, both rear and van. The Emperor rides on in wrath, and the Franks are full of care and foreboding; there is not a man but weepeth and maketh sore lament, praying to God that he spare Roland until they come unto the field, that at his side they may deal good blows. But what avails it? They have tarried too long, and may not come in time.

Charles the King rides on in great wrath, and over his hauberk is spread his white beard. And all the barons of France spur mightily, not one but is full of wrath and grief that he is not with Roland the captain who is at battle with the Saracens of Spain. If he be wounded, what hope that one soul be left alive? God, what a sixty he still hath in his fellowship; no king or captain ever had better.

Roland looks abroad over hill and heath and sees the great multitude of the Frankish dead, and he weeps for them as beseems a gentle knight, saying: "Lords and barons now may God have mercy upon you, and grant Paradise to all your

souls, that ye may rest among the blessed flowers.
Man never saw better men of arms than ye were.
Long and well, year in and year out, Roland
have ye served me, and many wide lands maketh
have ye won for the glory of Charles. lament
Was it to such an end that he nourished you? O
France, fair land, today art thou made desolate
by rude slaughter. Ye Frankish barons, I see ye
die through me, yet can I do naught to save or
defend you. May God, who knows no lie, aid you!
Oliver, brother, I must not fail thee; yet I shall
die of grief, and I be not slain by the sword. Sir
comrade, let us get us into battle."

So Count Roland falls a-smiting again. He
holds Durendal in his hand, and lays on right
valiantly, that he cleaves in twain Faldron de Pui,
and slays four and twenty of the most worshipful
of the paynims. Never shall ye see man more
desirous to revenge himself. And even as the
hart flies before the hounds, so flee the heathen
from before Roland. "Thou dost rightly," then
said the Archbishop; "such valour well beseems
a knight who bears arms and sits a good horse;
in battle such a one should be fell and mighty, or
he is not worth four deniers, and it behooves him
to turn monk and get him into a monastery to pray
the livelong day for our sins." And Roland answered him, saying: "Smite and spare not." And
at these words the Franks go into battle again;
but great is the slaughter of the Christians.

That man who knows he shall get no mercy defends him savagely in battle. Wherefore the Franks are fierce as lions. Marsila like a true baron sits his horse Gaignon; he spurs him well and rides on Bevon — lord he was of Beaune and Dijon — and breaks his shield, and rends his hauberk, that without other hurt he smites him dead to ground. And thereafter he slew Ivon and Ivory, and with them Gerard the Old of Roussillon. Now nigh at hand is Count Roland, and he saith to the paynim: "May the Lord God bring thee to mishap! And because thou hast wrongfully slain my comrades thou shalt thyself get a buffet before we twain dispart, and this day thou shalt learn the name of my sword." And therewith he rides upon him like a true baron, and smites off his right hand, and thereafter he takes off the head of Jurfaleu the Fair, the son of King Marsila. Thereat the paynims cry: "Now help us, Mahound! O ye, our gods, revenge us upon Charles! He has sent out against us into our marches men so fierce that though they die they will not give back." And one saith to another: "Let us fly." At these words a hundred thousand turn and flee, and let whosoever will, call them, they will not return again.

[King Marsila has lost his right hand; and now he throws his shield to earth, and pricks on his horse with his sharp spurs, and with slackened

Marsila aketh light (marginal note)

rein, flees away towards Spain. Upon twenty
thousand Saracens follow after him, nor is there
one among them who is not maimed or hurt of
body, and they say one to another: "The nephew
of Charles has won the field."]

But alack, what avails it? for though Marsila
be fled his uncle the Caliph yet abides, he who
ruled Aferne, Carthage, Garmalie, and Ethiopia,
a cursed land; under his lordship he has
the black folk, great are their noses and   The onset
of the
large their ears, and they are with him   Caliph
to the number of fifty thousand. And now they
come up in pride and wrath, and cry aloud the war-
cry of the paynims. Then saith Roland: "Now
must we needs be slain, and well I know we have
but a little space to live; but cursed be he who
doth not sell himself right dear. Lay on, lords,
with your burnished swords, and debate both life
and death; let not sweet France be brought to
shame through us. When Charles, my liege lord,
shall come into this field, he will see such slaughter
of the Saracens, that he shall find fifteen of them
dead over against each man of ours, and he will
not fail to bless us."

When Roland sees the cursed folk whose skin
is blacker than any ink, and who have naught of
white about them save their teeth, he saith:
"Now I know in very sooth that we shall die this
day. Lay on, lords, and yet again I bid thee,
smite." "Now foul fall him who lags behind,"

quoth Oliver.   And at this word the Franks haste into the fray.

Now when the paynims see how few are the Franks, they have great pride and joy thereof; and one saith to another: "Certes, the Emperor is in the wrong."   The Caliph bestrides a sorrel horse, he pricks him on with his spurs of gold, Oliver sore and smites Oliver from behind, amid hurt the back, that he drives the mails of his white hauberk into his body, and his lance passes out through his breast: "Now hast thou got a good buffet," quoth the Caliph.   "On an ill day Charles the Great left thee in the passes; much wrong hath he done us, yet he shall not boast thereof, for on thee alone have I well revenged us."

Oliver feels that he is wounded unto death; in his hand he holds Halteclere, bright was its blade, and with it he smites the Caliph on his golden pointed helmet, that its flowers and gems fall to earth, and he cleaves the head even unto the teeth, and with the force of the blow smote him dead to earth, and said: "Foul fall thee, paynim!   *Say not that I am come to my death through Charles;* and neither to thy wife, nor any other dame, shalt thou ever boast in the land from which thou art come, that thou hast taken from me so much as one farthing's worth, or hast done any hurt to me or to others."   And thereafter he called to Roland for succour.

Oliver feels that he is wounded unto death;
never will he have his fill of vengeance.   In the
thick of the press he smites valiantly, cleaving
lances and embossed shields, and feet and hands
and flanks and shoulders.   Whosoever saw him
thus dismember the Saracens, and hurl one dead
upon another, must call to mind true valiance;
nor did he forget the war-cry of Charles, but loud
and clear he cries out Montjoy!   And he calls to
Roland, his friend and peer: "Sir comrade, come
stand thou beside me.   In great dolour shall we
twain soon be disparted."

Roland looks Oliver in the face, pale it is and
livid and all discoloured; the bright blood flows
down from amid his body and falls in
streams to the ground.   "God," saith
the Count, "now I know not what to do.
Sir comrade, woe worth thy valour!   Never shall
the world see again a man of thy might.   Alas,
fair France, today art thou stripped of goodly
vassals, and fallen and undone.   The Emperor
will suffer great loss thereby."   And so speaking
he swoons upon his horse.

Lo, Roland has swooned as he sits his horse,
and Oliver is wounded unto death, so much has
he bled that his sight is darkened, and he can no
longer distinguish any living man whether far
off or near at hand; and now, as he meets his
comrade, he smites him upon the helm set with
gold and gems, and cleaves it down to the nasal,

but does not come unto the head. At the blow
Roland looks up at him, and asks him full softly
and gently: "Comrade, dost thou this wittingly?
I am Roland who so loves thee. Never yet hast
thou mistrusted me." Then saith Oliver: "Now
I hear thee speak, but I cannot see thee; may the
Lord God guard thee. I have struck thee, but I
pray thy pardon." "Thou hast done me no hurt,"
Roland answers him ; "I pardon thee before God,
as here and now." So speaking each leans forward towards other, and lo, in such friendship
they are disparted.

Oliver feels the anguish of death come upon
him; his two eyes turn in his head; and his hearing goes from him, and all sight. He lights down
from his horse and lies upon the ground, and
again and again he confesses his sins; he holds
out his clasped hands toward heaven and prays
God that he grant him Paradise, and he blesses
Charles and sweet France, and Roland, his comrade, above all men. Then his heart fails him,
and his head sinks upon his breast, and he lies
stretched at all his length upon the ground. Dead
is the Count and gone from hence. Roland weeps
for him and is sore troubled; never on the earth
shall ye see a man so sorrowful.

When Count Roland sees his friend lie prone
and dead, facing the East, gently he begins to
lament him: "Sir comrade, woe worth thy hardiness! We twain have held together for years and

days, never didst thou me wrong or I thee. Since
thou art dead, alack that I yet live." So speaking, the Count swoons as he sits Veillantif his
horse, but his golden spurs hold him firm, and
let him go where he will, he cannot fall.

So soon as Roland comes to his senses, and is
restored from his swoon, he is ware of the great
slaughter about him. Slain are the The coming
Franks, he has lost them all save only of Gualter
Gualter del Hum and the Archbishop. Gualter
has come down from the mountains where he
fought hardily with those of Spain; the paynims conquered, and his men are slain, and howsoever unwillingly, he must perforce flee down
into the valley and call upon Roland for succour.
"O gentle Count, brave captain, where art thou?
for where thou art I have no fear. It is I, Gualter, who conquered Maëlgut, I the nephew of
Droön the old, the hoary, I whom thou wert wont
to love for my hardihood. Now my shield is
pierced, and the shaft of my lance is broken, and
my hauberk rent and unmailed; I have the wounds
of eight lances in my body, and I must die, but
dear have I sold myself." So he saith, and Roland
hears him, and spurs his horse and rides towards
him.

["Sir Gualter," then saith Roland, "thou hast,
as I know, done battle with the paynims, and
thou art a hardy and valiant warrior. A thousand good knights thou didst take with thee, my

men they were, and now I would ask them of thee again; give them over to me, for sore is my need." But Gualter makes answer: "Never again shall ye see one of them alive. I left them on the dolourous field. We encountered a great host of Saracens, Turks and Armenians, Persians, and men of Canaan and of Lude, warriors of the best, mounted on swift Arabian horses. And we fought a battle so fierce that never a paynim shall boast thereof, sixty thousand lie dead and bleeding; and we, on our part, lost all our Franks, but vengeance we took therefor with our swords of steel. Rent and torn is my hauberk, and deadly wounds I have in side and flank, and from all my body flows out the bright blood, and takes from me my strength; certes, my time is nigh spent. Thy man am I, and I look to thee as protector. Blame me not, that I fled." "Nay, I blame thee no whit," quoth Count Roland. "But now do thou aid me, so long as thou art a living man."]

Full sorrowful is Roland and of great wrath; he falls a-smiting in the thick of the press, and of those of Spain he cast twenty to the ground dead, and Gualter slew six, and the Archbishop five. Then say the paynims: "Fierce and fell are these men. Take ye heed, lords, that they go not hence alive. He who doth not set upon them is traitor, and recreant he who lets them go hence." Then the hue and

The three Franks still make stand

cry begins again, and from all sides they close about the three Franks.

Count Roland is a full noble warrior, and a right good knight is Gualter del Hum, the Archbishop is of good valour and well tried; not one would leave aught to his fellows, and together, in the thick of the press, they smite the paynims. A thousand Saracens get them to foot, and there are still forty thousand on horseback, yet in sooth they dare not come nigh unto the three, but they hurl upon them lances and spears, arrows and darts and sharp javelins. In the first storm they slew Gualter, and sundered the shield of Turpin of Rheims, broke his helmet and wounded him in his head, and rent and tore his hauberk that he was pierced in the body by four spears; and his horse was slain under him. The Archbishop falls; great is the pity thereof.

But so soon as Turpin of Rheims finds himself beaten down to earth with the wounds of four lances in his body, he right speedily gets him afoot again; he looks toward Roland, and hastes to him, and saith: "I am nowise vanquished; no good vassal yields him so long as he is a living man." And he draws Almace, his sword of brown steel, and in the thick of the press he deals well more than a thousand buffets. Afterwards Charles bore witness that Turpin spared himself no whit, for around him they found four hundred dead, some wounded, some cut in twain amid the body.

and some whose heads had been smitten off; so saith the Geste and he who was on the field, the valiant Saint Gilles, for whom God wrought miracles; he it was who wrote the annals of the monastery of Laon. And he who knows not this, knows naught of the matter.

Count Roland fights right nobly, but all his body is a-sweat and burning hot, and in his head he hath great pain and torment, for when he sounded his horn he rent his temples. But he would fain know that Charles were coming, and he takes his horn of ivory, and feebly he sounds it. The Emperor stops to listen: "Lords," he saith, "now has great woe come upon us, this day shall we lose Roland my nephew, I wot from the blast of his horn that he is nigh to death. Let him who would reach the field ride fast. Now sound ye all the trumpets of the host." Then they blew sixty thousand, so loud that the mountains resound and the valleys give answer. The paynims hear them and have no will to laugh, but one saith to another: "We shall have ado with Charles anon."

The trumpets of France

Say the paynims: "The Emperor is returning, we hear the trumpets of France; if Charles come hither, we shall suffer sore loss. Yet if Roland live, our war will begin again, and we shall lose Spain our land." Then four hundred armed in their helmets, and of the best of those on the field, gather together, and on Roland they make onset fierce and sore. Now is the Count hard bestead.

When Count Roland sees them draw near he waxes hardy and fierce and terrible; never will he yield as long as he is a living man. He sits his horse Veillantif, and spurs him well with his spurs of fine gold, and rides into the stour upon them all; and at his side is Archbishop Turpin. And the Saracens say one to another: "Now save yourselves, friends. We have heard the trumpets of France; Charles the mighty King is returning."

Count Roland never loved the cowardly, or the proud, or the wicked, or any knight who was not a good vassal, and now he calls to Archbishop Turpin, saying: "Lord, thou art on foot and I am a-horseback, for thy love I would make halt, and together we will take the good and the ill; I will not leave thee for any living man; the blows of Almace and of Durendal shall give back this assault to the paynims." Then saith the Archbishop: "A traitor is he who doth not smite; Charles is returning, and well will he revenge us."

"In an evil hour," say the paynims, "were we born; woeful is the day that has dawned for us! We have lost our lords and our peers. Charles the valiant cometh hither again with his great host, we hear the clear trumpets of those of France, and great is the noise of their cry of Montjoy. Count Roland is of such

The flight of the Saracens

might he cannot be vanquished by any mortal man.
Let us hurl our missiles upon him, and then leave
him." Even so they did; and cast upon him many
a dart and javelin, and spears and lances and
feathered arrows. They broke and rent the shield
of Roland, tore open and unmailed his hauberk,
but did not pierce his body: but Veillantif was
wounded in thirty places, and fell from under the
Count, dead. Then the paynims flee, and leave
him; Count Roland is left alone and on foot.

The paynims flee in anger and wrath, and in
all haste they fare toward Spain. Count Roland
did not pursue after them, for he has lost his
horse Veillantif, and whether he will or no, is
left on foot. He went to the help of Archbishop
Turpin, and unlaced his golden helm from his
head, and took off his white hauberk of fine mail,
and he tore his tunic into strips and with the

Roland
seeketh the
Twelve
Peers pieces bound his great wounds. Then
he gathers him in his arms, and lays him
down full softly upon the green grass,
and gently he beseeches him: "O gracious baron,
I pray thy leave. Our comrades whom we so
loved are slain, and it is not meet to leave them
thus. I would go seek and find them, and range
them before thee." "Go and return again,"
quoth the Archbishop. "Thank God, this field
is thine and mine."

Roland turns away and fares on alone through
the field; he searches the valleys and the hills;

(and there he found Ivon and Ivory,) and Gerin, and Gerier his comrade, (and he found Engelier the Gascon,) and Berengier, and Oton, and he found Anseïs and Samson, and Gerard the Old of Rousillon.   One by one he hath taken up the barons, and hath come with them unto the Archbishop, and places them in rank before him.   The Archbishop cannot help but weep; he raises his hand and gives them benedic- <small>and Turpin gives them absolution</small> tion, and thereafter saith: "Alas for ye, lords! May God the Glorious receive your souls, and bring them into Paradise among the blessed flowers.   And now my own death torments me sore; never again shall I see the great Emperor."

Again Roland turned away to search the field; and when he found Oliver his comrade, he gathered him close against his breast, and as best he might returned again unto the Archbishop, and laid his comrade upon a shield beside the others; and the Archbishop absolved and blessed him. Then their sorrow and pity broke forth again, and Roland saith: "Oliver, fair comrade, thou wert son of the great Duke Reinier, who held the Marches of Rivier and Genoa; for the breaking of lances or the piercing of shields; for vanquishing and affrighting the proud, for upholding and counselling the good, never in any land was there a better knight."

When Roland sees the peers, and Oliver whom he so loved, lying dead, pity takes him and he begins to weep; and his face is all discoloured; so great is his grief he cannot stand upright, but will he, nill he, falls to the ground in a swoon. Saith the Archbishop: "Alack for thee, good baron."

When the Archbishop sees Roland swoon, he has such dole as he has never known before. He stretches out his hand and takes the horn of ivory, for in Roncevals there is a swift streamlet, and he would go to it to bring of its water to Roland.

The death of the Archbishop

Slowly and falteringly he sets forth, but so weak he is he cannot walk, his strength has gone from him, too much blood has he lost, and before a man might cross an acre his heart faileth, and he falls forward upon his face, and the anguish of death comes upon him.

When Count Roland recovers from his swoon he gets upon his feet with great torment; he looks up and he looks down, and beyond his comrades, on the green grass, he sees that goodly baron, the Archbishop, appointed of God in His stead. Turpin saith his *mea culpa*, and looks up, and stretches out his two hands towards heaven, and prays God that he grant him Paradise. And so he dies, the warrior of Charles. Long had he waged strong war against the paynims, both by his mighty battling and his goodly sermons. May God grant him his holy benison.

Count Roland sees the Archbishop upon the ground; his bowels have fallen out of his body, and his brains are oozing out of his forehead;

Roland takes his fair, white hands and crosses
them upon his breast between his two collar bones;
and lifting up his voice, he mourns for him, after
the manner of his people: "Ah gentle man, knight
of high parentage, now I commend thee to the
heavenly Glory; never will there be a man who
shall serve Him more willingly; never since the
days of the apostles hath there been such a pro-
phet to uphold the law, and win the hearts of
men; may thy soul suffer no dole or torment, but
may the doors of Paradise be opened to thee."

Now Roland feels that death is near him, and
his brains flow out at his ears; he prays to the
Lord God for his peers that He will receive them, and he prays to the Angel   Roland feel-
Gabriel for himself. That he may be   eth death
                                        near him
free from all reproach, he takes his horn of ivory
in the one hand, and Durendal, his sword, in the
other, and farther than a cross-bow can cast an
arrow, through a cornfield he goeth on towards
Spain. At the crest of a hill, beneath two fair
trees, are four stairs of marble; there he falls
down on the green grass in a swoon, for death is
close upon him.

High are the hills and very tall are the trees; the
four stones are of shining marble; and there Count
Roland swoons upon the green grass. Meantime
a Saracen is watching him; he has stained his
face and body with blood, and feigning death, he
lies still among his fellows; but now he springs

to his feet and hastens forward. Fair he was, and strong, and of good courage; and in his pride he breaks out into mighty wrath, and seizes upon Roland, both him and his arms, and he cries: "Now is the nephew of Charles overthrown. This his sword will I carry into Arabia." But at his touch the Count recovered his senses.

Roland feels that his sword hath been taken from him, he opens his eyes, and saith: "Certes, thou art not one of our men." He holds his horn of ivory which he never lets out of his grasp, and he smites the Saracen upon the helm which was studded with gold and gems, and he breaks steel and head and bones that his two eyes start out, and he falls down dead at his feet. Then saith Roland: "Coward, what made thee so bold to lay hands upon me, whether right or wrong? No man shall hear it but shall hold thee a fool. Now is my horn of ivory broken in the bell, and its gold and its crystals have fallen."

Now Roland feels that his sight is gone from him. With much striving he gets upon his feet; the colour has gone from his face; before him lies a brown stone, and in his sorrow and wrath he smites ten blows upon it. The sword *He would fain break his sword* grates upon the rock, but neither breaks nor splinters; and the Count saith: "Holy Mary, help me now! Ah Durendal, alas for your goodness! *Now am I near to death, and have no more need of you.* Many a fight in

the field have I won with you, many a wide land
have I conquered with you, lands now ruled by
Charles with the white beard. May the man who
would flee before another, never possess you. For
many a day have you been held by a right good
lord, never will there be such another in France
the free."

Roland smote upon the block of *hard stone*,
and the steel grates, but neither breaks nor splinters. And when he sees that he can in
nowise break it, he laments, saying: "O   He calleth
to mind his
Durendal, how fair and bright thou art,   conquests
in the sunlight how thou flashest and shinest!
Charles was once in the valley of Moriane, when
God commanded him by one of his angels that he
should give thee to a chieftain Count; then the
great and noble King girded thee upon me; and
with thee I won for him Anjou and Bretagne,
and I conquered Poitou and Maine for him, and
for him I conquered Normandy the free, and Provence, and Acquitaine; and Lombardy, and all
of Romagna; and I conquered for him Bavaria,
and Flanders, and Bulgaria, and all of Poland;
Constantinople which now pays him fealty, and
Saxony, where he may work his will. And I conquered for him Wales, and Scotland, and Ireland,
and England which he holds as his demesne.
Many lands and countries have I won with thee,
lands which Charles of the white beard rules. And
now am I heavy of heart because of this my sword;

rather would I die than that it should fall into the
hands of the paynims.   Lord God our Father, let
not this shame fall upon France."

And again Roland smote upon the brown stone
and beyond all telling shattered it; the sword
grates, but springs back again into the air and
is neither dinted nor broken.   And when the
Count sees he may in no wise break it, he laments,
saying: "O Durendal, how fair and holy a thing
thou art!   In thy golden hilt is many a relic, —
a tooth of Saint Peter, and some of the blood
of Saint Basil, and hairs from the head of my
lord, Saint Denis, and a bit of the raiment of the
Virgin Mary.   It is not meet that thou fall into
the hands of the paynims, only Christians should
wield thee.   May no coward ever possess thee!
Many wide lands have I conquered with thee,
lands which Charles of the white beard rules;
and thereby is the Emperor great and mighty."

Now Roland feels that death has come upon
him, and that it creeps down from his head to
his heart.   In all haste he fares under a pine
tree, and hath cast himself down upon his face on
the green grass.   Under him he laid his
sword and his horn of ivory; and he
turned his face towards the paynim folk,
for he would that Charles and all his men should
say that the gentle Count had died a conqueror.
Speedily and full often he confesses his sins, and
in atonement he offers his glove to God.

He turneth
his face
towards
Spain

ROLAND SOUNDING HIS HORN

Roland lies on a high peak looking towards Spain; he feels that his time is spent, and with one hand he beats upon his breast: "O God, I have sinned; forgive me through thy might the wrongs, both great and small, which I have done from the day I was born even to this day on which I was smitten." With his right hand he holds out his glove to God; and lo, the angels of heaven come down to him.

Count Roland lay under the pine tree; he has turned his face towards Spain, and he begins to call many things to remembrance, — all the lands he had won by his valour, and sweet France, and the men of his lineage, and Charles, his liege lord, who had brought him up in his household; and he cannot help but weep. But he would not wholly forget himself, and again he confesses his sins and begs forgiveness of God: "Our Father, who art truth, who raised up Lazarus from the dead, and who defended Daniel from the lions, save thou my soul from the perils to which it is brought through the sins I wrought in my life days." With his right hand he offers his glove to God, and Saint Gabriel has taken it from his hand. Then his head sinks on his arm, and with clasped hands he hath gone to his end. And God sent him his cherubim, and Saint Michael of the Seas, and with them went Saint Gabriel, and they carried the soul of the Count into Paradise.

PART III

THE VENGEANCE OF CHARLES

DEAD is Roland, God in heaven has his soul.
The Emperor has come into Roncevals.   There
is no road, nor path, nor open space of land,

Charles
cometh to
Roncevals though it be but the width of an ell or
the breadth of a foot, that is not strewn
with Franks or paynims.   And Charles
cries out: " Where art thou, fair nephew? Where
is Count Oliver, and where the Archbishop?
Where is Gerin, and Gerier his comrade? Where
is Oton the Duke, and Count Berengier, and Ivon
and Ivory whom I hold so dear?   What has be-
fallen Engelier the Gascon, Samson the Duke,
and Anseïs the Proud?   Where is Gerard the
Old of Rousillon?   Where are the Twelve Peers
that I left behind me?"   But what avails his call
since no one gives answer?   "O God," saith the
King, "much it weighs on me that I was not here
to begin the onset."   And he plucks at his beard
even as a man in wrath.   His knights and barons
weep, and twenty thousand fall swooning to the
ground; great is the sorrow of Naymes the Duke.

[Mighty is the woe at Roncevals.]   There is

no knight or baron but weeps right sore for pity.
They weep for their sons and brothers and neph-
ews, and for their friends, and for their liege
lords; many a one falls swooning to the ground
But Duke Naymes bears him like a man of valour,
he is the first to bespeak the Emperor, saying:
"Look two leagues before us, where on the dusty
highroad fares the throng of the paynim folk.
I prithee ride on and revenge this woe." "Ah
God," saith Charles, "already are they far from
us. Now grant me justice and honour. They
have taken from me the flower of sweet France."

Then the King commands Gebuin and Odo,
Tedbalt of Rheims and Count Milon, saying:
"Guard ye this field, the valleys and the mountains; let the dead lie even as they are, let not
the lions or any wild beast come nigh them,
neither the sergeants nor the varlets, let not any
man lay hands on them, until God grants us to
return to this field." And they answered him
gently in their love: "Just Emperor, dear lord,
even so will we do." And they keep with them
a thousand of their knights.

The Emperor bids the trumpets be sounded,
and then he rides on with his great host. They
have found the traces of those of Spain,
and they pursue after them, and all   He pursues
the pay-
nims
are of one mind. And when the King
sees the night coming on, he dismounts in a meadow of green grass, and casts himself upon the

ground, and prays to the Lord God that he make the sun to stand still for him, the darkness to delay and the light to abide.   And an angel that was wont to speak with him straightway commanded him, saying: "Charles, mount thy horse, and the light shall not fail thee.   Thou hast lost the flower of France, and this God knows; it is granted thee to revenge thyself upon this guilty folk."   At these words the Emperor gets him to horse.

For Charles God has wrought a great wonder; and the sun is stayed in the heavens.   The heathen flee, and fiercely the Franks pursue them; in Val Tenebres they come upon them; and with *and de-* their swords they drive them towards *stroys their* Saragossa, and slay them as they go with *army* great slaughter; and they cut them off from the roads and the footways.   The stream of the Ebro is before them, deep it is, and swift and terrible, and there is neither ferry nor barge nor dromond.   The paynims call upon their god Tervagant; then they leap into the stream, but find no safety.   The armed knights are the heaviest, and some among them sink to the bottom, others are swept along by the current, and even those who fare best drink deep of the water; all alike are miserably drowned.   And the Franks cry to them, saying: "Woe worth the day ye saw Roland!"

When Charles sees that all the paynims are

dead, some slain by the sword, and the more part
drowned — great was the booty his knights had
of them — the gentle King dismounts, and casts
himself upon the ground and gives thanks to God.
When he again gets upon his feet the sun is
set. "Time it is to make encampment," he saith;
"too late it is to return again to Roncevals. Our
horses are weary and spent; take off their saddles
and bridles, and let them graze in the meadows."
"Lord, thou sayest well and truly," the Franks
make answer.

The Emperor has made stay for the night.
The Franks dismount beside the Ebro; they un-
saddle their horses and take the golden
bridles from off their heads, and they   The Franks
                                          encamp by
                                          Ebro
turn them into meadows of fresh grass;
no other cheer can they make them.   Those who
are weary sleep upon the ground; that night no
guard was set.

The Emperor lies him down in the meadow; at
his head he puts his great lance; this night he will
not disarm himself, but dons his white hauberk,
laces his gold-adorned helmet, and girds on Joyeuse, — never was there its like, thirty times a
day it changes its light.   Much we might tell
you of the spear with which Our Lord was pierced
upon the cross; Charles has the point thereof,
thanks be to God, and has encased it in the
golden hilt of his sword; for this honour and ex-
cellence it has been called Joyeuse.   The barons

of France should hold this in mind, for from this, they took their cry of Montjoy; and thus it is that no folk can withstand them.

Clear is the night and fair the moon. Charles lies upon the ground, but is full of dole for Roland, and right heavy of heart because of Oliver, and the Twelve Peers, and the Frankish folk that he has left at Roncevals dead and stained with blood; he cannot help but weep and make lament, and he prays God that He save their souls. Weary is the King, for his woe is very great, and he sleeps, he cannot help but sleep. Now throughout all the fields the Franks lie at rest; nor is there a horse with strength to stand upon his feet, if any wishes grass he takes it as he lies. Much has he learned who knows sorrow.

Charles sleeps like a man spent with toil and grief. God sent Saint Gabriel to him, and bid him guard the Emperor. All night the angel watched by his pillow, and in a vision he made known to him a battle which is to be levied against him and the grave import thereof. Charles looks up into the heavens, and sees thunder and cold and whirlwinds, storms and mighty tempests, and fire and flame are kindled there; and all these straightway fall upon his people. The fire burns their lances of oak and apple wood, and their shields even to the bosses of pure gold; the shafts of their sharp lances are shattered, and their hauberks and helmets of steel

Of the two visions of Charles

are destroyed. Sore bestead are his knights, lions
and leopards are ready to devour them, serpents
and vipers, dragons, and devils; and of griffons
there are more than thirty thousand; and all these
fall upon the Franks. They cry: "Help us,
Charles!" The King is full of grief and pity for
their sake, and would fain go to them, but he is
withheld; for from without the wood comes a
great lion proud and mighty and fierce, he sets
upon the King's self, and each clasps other in the
struggle; but who conquers and who falls is not
made plain. Still the Emperor does not waken.

Thereafter came another vision to him, and it
seemed to him that he was at Aix in France on a
terrace, and was holding a bear in a double chain,
when he saw coming from Ardennes thirty more
bears, who spoke to him as they had been men,
saying: "Give him to us again, lord, it is not just
that ye withhold him from us; it is our part to
rescue our kinsman." But even then from without the palace ran a deerhound and set upon the
greatest of the bears, a little apart from his fellows on the green grass. Then saw the King
a wondrous battle, but he knew not which won
or which failed therein. These things God's
angel made manifest to the baron. And Charles
slept even to bright day.

King Marsila has fled away to Saragossa, and
lights down from his horse under the shade of an
olive, he takes off sword and helmet and byrnie,

and casts himself all woe-begone upon the green grass. He has lost his right hand and swoons Marsila comes again to Saragossa from pain and loss of blood. Beside him Bramimonde, his wife, weeps and makes lament, bitterly she bemoans herself; and with her are more than thirty thousand men who all curse Charles and fair France.

They haste to their god Apollon in a grotto hard by, and upbraid him, and lay rude hands upon him, saying: "O cruel god, why hast thou brought this shame upon us? why hast thou let our King be vanquished? An ill reward thou givest him who has served thee well." Then they took away his sceptre and his crown, (and dragged him down from the column with their hands,) and trod him to earth under their feet; with great staves they beat him and brake him to bits. And they robbed Tervagant of his carbuncle; and they cast Mahound into a ditch, for the dogs and the pigs to worry and gnaw.

Marsila has recovered from his swoon, and they have brought him into his vaulted chamber, painted and inscribed with many colours. And Bramimonde the Queen weeps for him, tears her hair, and makes great moan. Then she lifts up her voice and cries aloud: "O Saragossa, now art thou made desolate of the gentle King who held thee in fee. Traitors to him were the gods who failed him this day in battle. The Amiral will do cowardly, an he does not set upon this bold

people, who are so proud they have no care for
life or death. The Emperor of the hoary beard
is valiant and of good courage; if there be a battle he will not flee the field. Woe it is there is
none to slay him."

The Emperor by his might has abode for seven
long years in Spain; he has taken its castles and
many a city. King Marsila has striven against
him; and in the first year he let seal letters, and
sent them to Baligant in Babylon — he is the old
Amiral of antiquity who has outlived   Baligant the
Homer and Virgil — that he come with   Amiral
  gathers his
succour to Saragossa; if he comes not,   host
Marsila swears he will forsake his gods and all
the idols he was wont to worship, and will receive
the Christian faith, and will make peace with
Charles. But the Amiral is afar off and has tarried long. From forty kingdoms he has summoned his people; he has had his great dromonds
made ready, his boats and barges and galleys and
ships; all his fleet he has gathered together at his
port of Alexandria. It is in May, on the first
day of summer, that all his armies embark on
the sea.

Great is the host of this hostile folk, and swiftly
they steer with sail and oar. On the yards and
topmasts are hung many a lantern and carbuncle,
and from on high they shed forth such a bright-
ness that by night the sea is yet more fair. And
as they draw near to the land of Spain all the

countryside is lighted thereby and illumed ; and
the news thereof comes to Marsila.

The paynim folk would make no stay, they leave
the sea and come into fresh water; they leave behind them Marbrise and Marbruse, and pass with
all their ships up the Ebro.   They have lanterns
and carbuncles without number, which give them
light all the night through.   And with the day
they come to Saragossa.

Fair is the day and bright the sun.   The Amiral has left his ship; at his right hand walks
Baligant   Espanelis and seventeen kings follow
sweareth the   after him, and counts and dukes I know
death of
Charles   not how many.   Under a laurel tree,
amid an open field, they spread a cloth of white
silk upon the green grass, and by it they placed
a throne of ivory whereon sits the paynim Baligant, and all the rest stand about him.   Their
lord was the first to speak: "Now hearken brave
knights and free: Charles, the Emperor of the
Franks, must eat no more, unless I so command
it.   He has waged strong war upon me throughout all Spain; and now I would seek him in fair
France, nor will I rest my life long until he be
slain, or yields him alive."   And with his glove
he smites his right knee.

So said he, and maintains that for all the gold
under heaven he will not fail to go unto Aix, where
Charles is wont to hold his court.   And his men
gave him counsel and praised him.   Then he called

two of his knights, Clarien and Clarifan, saying:
"Ye are sons of King Maltraïen who was ever a
ready messenger; and now I command you that
you go unto Saragossa, and say to Marsila that I
am come to aid him against the Franks, if I come
upon their host, great will be the battle. Give him
now this glove embroidered with gold, give it into
his right hand, and take to him this baton of pure
gold, and let him come to me to do me homage.
And thereafter I will go into France to war upon
Charles; if he doth not fall at my feet and cry my
mercy, and doth not forsake the faith of the Christians, I will strip the crown from off his head."
"Well said, lord," the paynims make answer.

"Now fare ye forth, barons," saith Baligant;
"let one carry the glove, the other the staff."
"Even so will we do, dear lord," they   He sends
make answer. So they rode forth till   promise of
                                         succour to
they came unto Saragossa. They pass   Marsila
ten gates and cross four bridges, and fare through
the streets where dwell the burgesses. As they
draw nigh to the upper city they hear a mighty
noise from about the palace, where a great throng
of the paynims are weeping and making great
dole; and they cry out upon their gods Tervagant
and Mahound and Apollon, who have no whit
availed them. And one saith to another: "Woe
is me, what will become of us? Now are we undone, for we have lost King Marsila, yesterday
Roland smote off his right hand; and Jurfaleu the

Fair hath been taken from us; and now all Spain will fall into the hands of the Franks." Meantime the two messengers dismount at the stairway.

They have left their horses under an olive tree; two Saracens took the bridles, and the messengers, each holding the other's mantle, mounted to the highest palace. As they enter the vaulted chamber they give greeting to Marsila in all friendship: "May Mahound who hath us in his power, and our lord Apollon, and Tervagant save the King and keep the Queen." "Ye speak folly," then saith Bramimonde, "for these our gods have proved recreant; little virtue they showed at Roncevals; they let our knights be slain,

Bramimonde maketh lament

and failed my lord in battle, he has lost his right hand, smitten off it was by Roland the mighty Count. Anon Charles will have all Spain in his power. What will become of me, caitiff and wretched? Ah me, if some man of ye would but slay me!"

"Dame," saith Clarien, "be not so full of words. Messengers are we from the paynim Baligant; he will save Marsila, he saith, and sends him his glove and staff. In the Ebro he hath four thousand shallops, boats, and barges, and swift galleys; and dromonds he hath without number. The Amiral is strong and mighty, he will go into France to seek out Charles, and he thinks to either slay him or make him yield him." "No need to go so far," quoth Bramimonde, "nigh at hand will you find the Franks. The Emperor hath been seven full years in this land; he is a valiant and great warrior, rather would he die than fly the field; no King under heaven is there whom he doth not hold as a child. Charles fears no man living."

"Nay, let be," saith King Marsila. And he turns to the messengers: "Speak ye to me, lords. Ye see that I am hurt to death; and I have neither son nor daughter nor heir, — one I had who was slain yesterday at eventide. Say ye to my liege lord that he come hither to me. He has rights upon this land of Spain, and I will give it over to him, if he would have it so; then let him defend it against the Franks. Concerning Charles I will give him good counsel, and mayhap by this day month he will have conquered him. Take to him the keys of Saragossa, and bid him go not far from hence, an he would take my counsel." "Lord thou speakest well and truly," they make answer.

Quoth Marsila: "Charles the Emperor hath slain my men, and laid waste my land, sacked and despoiled my cities; (and now his men are assembled on the banks of the Ebro), not more than seven leagues from here, as I deem it. Tell the Amiral to bring up his hosts and do him battle, so charge him from me." Then Marsila gave over to them the keys of Saragossa; and both messengers bow before him, and take their leave and go thence.

The two messengers have mounted their horses, swiftly they ride forth from the city, and come to the Amiral, sore troubled ; and they give over to

him the keys of Saragossa. "What news have ye?" saith Baligant. "Where is Marsila whom I summoned?" "He is hurt unto death," Clarien makes answer. "Yesterday Charles set forth through the passes, for he thought to return again to fair France. For his honour he set behind him a rearguard, and with it staid Count Roland, his nephew, and Oliver, and all the Twelve Peers, together with twenty thousand armed knights of France. King Marsila did them battle like a true baron, and in the field he and Roland fought together man to man, and Roland gave him so mighty a blow with Durendal that his right hand was smitten from off his body; and his son whom he so loved was slain, and likewise the barons he had in his company. He fled, for he could no longer make stand, and the Emperor pursued him full hotly. The King bids you come to his succour, and gives over into your hands the kingdom of Spain." And Baligant falls a-thinking; so great dole he has thereof that he wellnigh goes out of his senses.

"My lord Amiral," then saith Clarien, "yesterday a battle was fought at Roncevals. Dead are Roland and Count Oliver, and the Twelve Peers whom Charles held so dear, together with twenty thousand of the knights of France. There

King Marsila lost his right hand, and fiercely did
Charles pursue after him; and no knights are left
alive in this land, all are either slain or drowned
in the Ebro. On its banks the Franks have now
their camp, so near have they come to us in our
marches, but if you so will it, their retreat shall
be sore." And now Baligant is proud of look,
and is glad and joyous of heart; he rises from his
great chair, and cries aloud: "Barons, tarry not;
leave the ships, mount and ride! If Charles the
Old flee not before us King Marsila shall be revenged upon him; in return for his right hand I
will bring him a head."

The paynims of Arabia have come forth from
their ships, they have mounted their horses and
mules, and thereafter they rode forward,
— how else should they do? When he   The paynims
had set them on the march, the Amiral   ride to meet
                                         Charles
called Gemalfin, his dear friend, saying: "Lead
thou all my host, I command thee." Then he
mounted his brown war horse, and bid four dukes
follow him, and together they rode on till they
came unto Saragossa. By the marble stairway
he has lighted down from his horse, and four counts
hold his stirrup. As he mounts the stair of the
palace, Bramimonde runs forth to meet him, and
saith: "Woe worth the day on which I was born,
for now in shameful wise have I lost my lord!"
She falls at the feet of the Amiral, but he raises
her up, and sorrowfully they went up into the
chamber.

When King Marsila saw Baligant he called to him two Saracens of Spain, saying: "Put your arms about me that I may sit up." Then he took one of his gloves in his left hand, and said: "My lord and Amiral, I hereby give over all my land unto you, both Saragossa and all its dependencies. I have lost both my life and my folk." And the Amiral answered him: "For this am I right sorry. But I may not stay now for more words with thee, for full well I know Charles will not stay for us; yet none the less I will accept thy glove of thee." And for pity he weeps as he turns away. Then he hastes down the stair of the palace, mounts his horse and spurs as fast as he may back to his own folk. So fast he rode that he comes up with the foremost; and ever and again he cries aloud: "Haste ye, paynims, for even now the Franks flee before us."

In the morning, when the first dawn brightens, Charles the Emperor awakes. Saint Gabriel, who by God's command has guarded him, stretches out his hand and makes the sign of the cross upon him. The King has risen, and laid aside his armour, and all the men of the host likewise disarm themselves. Then they mount, and ride right speedily by long paths and wide ways, for they go to see the dread carnage at Roncevals where was the battle.

Charles is come into Roncevals. He begins to weep because of the dead he finds there, and he

saith to the Franks: "Barons, ride softly, for I
would go on before, to seek my nephew,
whom I myself would find. Once at
Aix, *at the feast of Christmas*, when my
good knights were boasting of great battles and
of fierce onsets, I heard Roland speak his mind,
saying, that if he should hap to die in a strange
land, it would be at the head of his men and his
peers, and his face would be turned to the land
of his foes, and he would die as a conqueror, the
baron." And farther than a man may throw a
staff, before all the rest Charles rides on up the
mountain.

The return to Roncevals

As the Emperor went seeking his nephew,
he found the grass and the flowers of the field
bright red with the blood of his barons. Great
pity he has thereof, and he may not help but
weep. He has come up the hill to the two trees,
full well he knew Roland's blows on the three
stairs, and he sees his nephew lying stretched
on the green grass. No wonder is it that Charles
is full of wrath. He lights down from his horse,
and runs to Roland and gathers him in his arms;
and he swoons over him so great is his grief.

The Emperor has recovered from his swoon;
and Naymes the Duke and Count Acelin, Geoffrey
of Anjou, and his brother Thierry take the King
and help him to sit up under a pine tree. He
looks to the ground and sees his nephew lying
there, and begins softly to lament him: "Dear

Roland, may God have mercy upon thee! For the arraying and winning of great battles, never has the world seen thy like. My glory is near to its setting." And Charles cannot help but swoon again.

Charles the King has recovered from his swoon, four of his barons hold him in their arms; he looks to the ground and sees his nephew lying dead, still strong and gallant of seeming, but his colour is gone, and his eyes, which have turned upwards, are darkened. Charles makes lament for him in all faith and love: "Dear Roland, may God bring thy soul among the flowers of Paradise, amid the glorious. Woe worth the day thou camest into Spain, baron! Never shall the day dawn whereon I shall not grieve for thee. Now my pride and my power will pass; for who henceforth will uphold my kingdom? In all the world I do not think to have a single friend; though I have other kindred none are valiant as thou wert." With both his hands he plucks the hair of his head; and so great is the dole of the Franks, that of a hundred thousand men there is not one that doth not weep.

"Dear Roland, I shall go back into France, and when I am come to Laon, to my great hall there, strange men will come to me from many lands, and they will ask of me where is the Count, the great chieftain, and I shall say to them that he lies dead in Spain. Thenceforth in sorrow shall I maintain my kingdom; never shall the day dawn whereon I shall not mourn for thee.

"Dear Roland, brave captain, fair youth, when I am come to Aix, to my chapel there, men will come to me asking news, and I shall tell them marvellous and heavy news: 'My nephew, who has conquered many lands for me, is dead.' Then the Saxons will rise up against me, and the Hungarians and the Bulgarians, and many hostile people, the Romans and the Apulians, and all those of Palermo, and those of Africa and those of Californe; then my woes and troubles will increase; for who will lead my armies against such a host when he is dead who was ever our champion? Ah fair France, how art thou made desolate! So great is my sorrow that gladly would I lay down my life." With both hands the King plucks his white beard and the hairs of his head. And a hundred thousand Franks fall swooning to the ground.

"Dear Roland, woe worth thy life days! May thy soul be brought into Paradise. He who slew thee wrought shame to sweet France. Now is my grief so great that I would not outlive those of my household who lie dead for my sake. May God, the son of Mary, grant that before I am come to the pass of Cizre, my soul may part from my body, and follow their souls, and that my body may be laid in the earth beside their bodies." And the King weeps and plucks his white beard. "Now great is the wrath of Charles," quoth Naymes the Duke.

"My lord and Emperor," then saith Geoffrey of Anjou, "make ye not such great dole; rather let the field be searched and our dead, whom those of Spain have slain in battle, be brought together in a common grave." "Now blow thy horn," the King makes answer.

Geoffrey of Anjou has sounded his horn; and the Franks light down from their horses, so Charles hath bidden it. And all their comrades The burial which they find dead they straightway of the dead. bring to the fosse. Many a bishop and abbot is there, and monks and canons and tonsured priests, and they have absolved the dead, and blessed them in God's name. And they kindled myrrh and sweet spices, and richly they perfumed them with incense, and buried them with great honour; and then they left them — how else should they do?

But the Emperor had Roland and Oliver and Archbishop Turpin laid apart from the rest, and he ordered their bodies to be opened in his presence, and had their hearts wrapped in silken cloths, and placed in caskets of white marble. Then they took the bodies of the three barons, and when they had washed them well with wine and spices, they wrapped them in hide of the deer. And the King commanded Tedbalt and Gebuin, Count

Milon, and Odo the Marquis, saying: "Carry ye them upon the march in three wains." Richly were they covered over with silk of Galaza.

And now, even as Charles would set forth, the vanguard of the paynims is upon him. From the foremost ranks ride forth two messengers, and in the name of the Amiral announce the battle: "Haughty King, flight now were cowardly. Lo, Baligant is upon thee, and great are the hosts he brings with him out of Arabia; this day we shall try thy valiance." The King plucks at his beard, and calls to mind his grief and his great loss; proudly he looks on his men, and lifting up his voice, which is great and mighty, he calls to them, saying: "Ye barons of France, now arm yourselves and get ye to horseback!"

The Franks make them ready for battle

The Emperor is the first to take arms; speedily has he donned his hauberk and laced his helmet, and girded on Joyeuse whose light outshines the sun, and now about his neck he hangs a shield of Gironde, and takes his lance which was fashioned at Blandonne, and then he mounts Tencendur, his good horse that he won at the ford below Marsonne, when he struck down and slew Malpalin of Narbonne; he slackens rein, and he spurs his horse that he springs and curvets before the eyes of a hundred thousand men. And he cries upon God and the Apostle of Rome.

Throughout the field the Franks light down

from their horses, and more than a hundred thousand don their armour; harness they have which well becomes them, and swift horses and goodly arms. As men well skilled they sprang to the saddle; if they meet with the paynim host, hardily will they do them battle. And their gonfanons sweep down to their helmets. Now when Charles sees their goodly bearing, he bespeaks Jozeran of Provence, Naymes the Duke and Antelme of Maïence, saying: "In such vassals a man may well set his trust, with them at his side it were folly to be dismayed. If the Arabs do not repent them of the battle, Roland's death shall cost them dear." "Now may God grant it to be as thou sayest," Naymes makes answer.

Then Charles calls Rabel and Guineman, saying: "Lords, I would have you be to me in the stead of Roland and Oliver; let one of you bear the sword, the other the horn of ivory, and do *Of the arraying of the ten companies* ye lead the host, taking with you fifteen thousand Franks, young men and of our most valiant. After these shall be as many more whom Gebuin and Lorent shall lead." Naymes the Duke and Count Jozeran array these battles; if they come upon the paynims, great will be the slaughter.

These first divisions are of men of France, but after these two a third is arrayed of the vassals of Bavaria, their knights they reckon at twenty thousand, and never will battle be shunned by them; there is no folk in all the world whom Charles holds so dear, save those of France who have conquered the kingdoms of the earth. Count Ogier the Dane, the great warrior, will lead them, for they are a haughty fellowship.

Thus Charles has already three companies. Then Naymes the Duke establishes a fourth of right valiant barons; Germans are they, the bravest of their folk, and they are reckoned at twenty thousand; well provided are they with horses and arms; never for fear of death would they flee the battle. Their leader is Herman Duke of Thrace; rather would he die than do cowardly.

Naymes the Duke and Count Jozeran have made up the fifth division of Normans; they number twenty thousand, so say the Franks; goodly are their arms and swift their horses; never for fear of death will they prove recreant; there is no folk under heaven more valiant in battle. Richard the Old will lead them to the field, and there will he deal good blows with his sharp spear.

The sixth battle is of Bretons, and forty thousand knights they number; straight are their lances and well fixed their gonfanons. Eudes is their over-lord, and he commands Count Nivelon, Tedbalt of Rheims and Odo the Marquis, saying: "Lead ye my folk, I give them into your hands."

Thus the Emperor has six battles arrayed.

Thereafter Naymes the Duke establishes the seventh of Poitevins and barons of Auvergne; they number upon forty thousand knights, good are their horses and fair their arms. They stand apart, in a valley, under a hillock, and Charles stretches out his right hand to them and blesses them. Their leaders are Jozeran and Godselme.

And now Naymes establishes the eighth battle of Flemings and of barons of Friesland; more than forty thousand knights they number, and never will they flee the field. "Well will they serve me," saith the King; "and Rembald and Hamon de Galice shall lead them in all knightliness."

Together Naymes and Count Jozeran array the ninth battle of brave warriors, men of Lorraine and Burgundy, knights to the number of fifty thousand; they have laced on their helmets and donned their byrnies, stout are their lances and short of shaft. If the Arabs hold not back from the encounter, these men will give them good blows; and Thierry the Duke of Argonne will lead them.

The tenth battle is of barons of France, a hundred thousand of our noblest knights, hardy of body and proud of bearing, hoary of head and white of beard, clad in hauberks and two-fold byrnies, girt with swords of France or Spain, and bearing shields with divers devices. They mount their horses

The Franks are fain of battle

and clamour for battle, crying out Montjoy. With them is Charles. Geoffrey of Anjou bears the oriflamme. Saint Peter's ensign it was, and thence had been called Romaine, but this day its name was changed to Montjoy.

The Emperor lights down from his horse, and throws himself upon the green grass, he turns his face to the rising sun and calls upon God with all his soul: "O our true Father, defend me this day, thou who saved Jonah from the whale in whose belly he was, and spared the King of Nineveh, and rescued Daniel from the dread torment of the lions' den, and preserved the three children in the fiery furnace. Let thy love be with me this day; and grant me in thy mercy, if it be thy will, that I may revenge Roland my nephew." And when he had prayed, he rose up, and upon his forehead made the sign which has so great power. Then the King mounts his swift horse, — Naymes and Jozeran held his stirrup for him, — and he takes his shield and sharp lance. He is full noble of person, comely and strong, clear of face and goodly of bearing. Then he rides forward right firmly. In rear and van the trumpets are sounded, and clear above the rest resounds the horn of ivory. And the Franks weep in pity for Roland.

The Emperor rides forward right nobly; he has spread out his beard over his hauberk, and for love of him the rest have done likewise, and thereby the hundred thousand Franks are known to all. They pass rocky cliffs and heights, deep val-

They seek the paynims

leys and dread defiles, and at last come beyond the passes and the waste lands, into the marches of Spain, and there on a space of level ground, they make halt. Meantime Baligant's advance-guard returns to him, and a Syrian among them tells his message: "We have seen Charles the haughty King, proud are his men, no mind have they to fail him. Arm yourselves, anon we shall have battle." Then saith Baligant: "Ye bring brave tidings. Sound your trumpets, that my paynims may know thereof."

Throughout all the host tabours are sounded, bussynes and clear trumpets. The paynims dismount and arm themselves. The Amiral would have no delay; he dons his hauberk, the skirt whereof is broidered and fringed, laces on his helmet adorned with gold; then he girds his

The might of the Amiral

sword at his left side, in his pride he has found a name for it, because of the sword of Charles whereof he has heard,

(and his he now calls Precieuse;) and he has made it his war-cry in the field, and has bidden his knights to cry it. And about his neck he hangs his shield which is wide and great, the boss thereof is gold and the border of precious stones, and its guige is of goodly silk patterned with roses. He grasps his lance which he calls Maltet, its shaft was as thick and great as a club, and the iron point thereof was as much as a mule might carry. Marcule from over-sea holds the stirrup as Baligant mounts his charger. Wide is the fork of the baron's legs, thin his flanks and great his sides; deep of chest he is, and well made of body, broad are his shoulders, and clear is his forehead, proud is his look and his hair right curly; and white he is as is the flower in summer time. Many a time has his prowess been proved. God, he were a goodly vassal, an he had but Christianity. He spurs his horse that the bright blood flows out, he sets him at a gallop and leaps a ditch which measures a good fifty feet. And the paynims cry: "Well he will defend our marches. The Frank who encounters with him, will he, nill he, must take his end. Charles is mad in that he has not fled."

The Amiral looks a goodly baron; white is his beard even as is the flower. And wise he is according to his law, and in battle he is fierce and mighty. His son Malpramis is full knightly, tall he is and strong and like to the men of his line. He saith to his father: "Lord, let us ride forward! much I doubt me if we see aught of Charles." "Yea, for he is a man of prowess," Baligant makes answer. "Great honour is done him in many a story; but now that he is bereft of Roland, his nephew, he will not have the might to withstand us."

"Malpramis, fair son," saith Baligant again,

"yesterday was slain Roland the good knight, and Oliver the wise, the valiant, and the Twelve Peers whom Charles held so dear, and with them twenty thousand warriors of France. Those that are left I rate at less than my glove. Yet sooth it is that the Emperor has returned hither again, so the Syrian, my messenger tells me, and that he has arrayed ten great battles. Right valiant is he who sounds the horn of ivory; with a clear trumpet his comrade answers him again, and together they ride at the head of the host; and with them are fifteen thousand Franks, young warriors whom Charles calls his children. And after these come as many more, and they will lay on right fiercely." Then saith Malpramis: "Lord, let the first blow be mine."

Malpramis
craves the
first blow

"Malpramis, fair son," answers Baligant, "I grant thee thy boon. Go, and fall anon upon the Franks, and take with thee Torleu the King of Persia, and Dapamort the King of Leutis. If thou canst mate the great pride of the Franks I will give thee a part of my kingdom from Cheriont even to Val-Marchis." "Lord, I thank thee," Malpramis made answer, and stood forth to receive the gift, — the land it was which aforetime King Flurit held — but never from that day was Malpramis to see it, never was he to be vested therein and installed.

And now the Amiral rides through the host.

and his son, who is tall of stature, follows him
with the two Kings, Torleu and Dapamort.
Quickly they array thirty great companies, and so
great is the multitude of his knights that the least
of these numbers thirty thousand men. The first
is arrayed of men of Botentrot, and the second
of Milciani, — they have huge heads, and along
the spine of their backs grow bristles like those
of a wild boar. The third is of Blos and of Nu-
bians; the fourth of Slavs and Russians; the fifth
is of the Sorbi; the sixth of Moors and Armenians; the seventh of men of Jericho; The Amiral
the eighth of Blacks and the ninth of arrayeth
                                                thirty
Gros; and the tenth is made up of men battles
of Balide-la-Forte, a folk that loves evil. Then
the Amiral swears a great oath by the might and
the body of Mahound: "Mad is Charles of France
to ride forward; a battle there will be, if he doth
not give back; and nevermore shall he wear golden crown on head."

Thereafter they array another ten battles; the
first is of the men of Canelieu, — they have
come across from Val-Fuit, and full hideous are
they to look upon; the second is of Turks; and
of Persians the third; the fourth is made up *of
fierce* Pincenati; the fifth of Soltras and Avars;
and the sixth of Ormaleus and Uglici; the seventh is arrayed of the people of Samuel; the
eighth is of the men of Prussia; the ninth of
Slavs, and the tenth of warriors of the desert of

Occiant, — a folk they are who do no service to the Lord God, never shall you hear of men more evil; and their skins are hard like iron, wherefore they have no need of hauberks or helms; and in battle they are fell and cruel.

Now the Amiral arrays another ten battles. The first is of the Giants of Malpruse; the second of Huns, and the third of Hungarians; in the fourth ride the folk of Baldise-la-Longue, and in the fifth those of the Dread Valley; the sixth is made up of men of Joi and of Maruse; the seventh of Lechs and Astrimunies; the eighth is of warriors of Arguille; the ninth of those of Clarbonne; and in the tenth ride the bearded folk of Val Fronde, — they are a people who have no love of God. So in the chronicles of France are named the thirty columns. Great are the hosts, and many a trumpet is sounded. The paynims ride on like goodly warriors.

Great and mighty is the Amiral; before him he lets bear the Dragon, and the standard of Tervagant and Mahound, and an image of Apollon the felon. Enclosing these ride ten men of Canelieu, and with a loud voice they cry: "Let those who would have the protection of our gods pray to them and serve them in all contrition!" And the paynims bow their heads, and bend full low their bright helmets. But the Franks cry: "Now die, ye swine! May ye be brought to confusion this day. And

Goodly are the two hosts

thou, our God, be Charles's shield, and let the battle be adjudged in his name."

Crafty and wise is the Amiral; he calls his son and the two Kings, saying: "Barons ride on before, and lead all my host; but three companies, and of the best, I keep with me, that of the Turks, and that of the Ormalies, and for the third, the Giants of Malpruse. And the men of Occiant shall abide with me, and they shall set upon Charles and his Franks. If the Emperor will do battle with me his head shall be severed from his body, let him be assured thereof, for such is his deserving."

Great are the two hosts and goodly the columns. Between them is neither hill nor height nor valley, neither holt nor forest, no hiding can there be, for each is clear to other in the open plain. Then saith Baligant: "Ride on, my paynims, and seek the battle!" Amboire d'Oluferne bears the standard; and the paynims lift up their voices, and cry aloud "Precieuse!" But the Franks make answer: "This day shall ye be given over to destruction!" And again and again they raise the cry of Montjoy. The Emperor bids his trumpets be sounded, and clear above them all rings out the horn of ivory. "Goodly is Charles's host," say the paynims; "great and sore will be the battle."

Vast is the plain and wide the fields. There s great shining of helmets adorned with gold, of

shields and broidered hauberks, of lances and gonfanons.   Trumpets blow, right clear are their
blasts, and high is the swell of the ivory horn.
The Amiral calls to his brother, Canabeu, the
King of Floredée, who held all the land even to
Val Sevrée, and showed him the ten companies
of Charles: "See the glory of France, the far-
famed; proudly rides the Emperor, he is behind
among the bearded folk; they have spread out
their beards over their hauberks, white they are
as is snow on ice.   These men will deal good
blows with lance and sword, great and terrible
will be the battle, such a one as was never before
seen of men."   Then farther than a man can
throw a peeled wand, Baligant rode out
Baligant
encourageth before his army, and bespoke them, say-
his men
ing: "Follow, for I lead, O paynims!"
And he hath shaken the shaft of his lance, and
turned its point towards Charles.

   When Charles the Great saw the Amiral, his
Dragon and ensign and standard, and the great
host of the Arabs, how that they covered all the
plain save that part which the Emperor himself
held, he cried out with a loud voice: "Barons of
France, good vassals are ye, and many are the
battles ye have fought in the field; see now the
paynims before you, felons they are and cowards,
and their faith avails them no whit; so though
their number be great, what care ye, lords? Let
him who would fain ride forward follow me."

Then he spurred his horse, and Tencendur sprang four times into the air. And the Franks say: "Valiant is our King. Ride on, lord, not one of us shall fail you."

Fair was the day and bright the sun; goodly the hosts and mighty the columns. And now the foremost ranks join battle. Count Rabel and Count Guineman slacken rein, and spur on their swift horses; and all the Franks drive forward, and fall a-smiting with their sharp spears. *The two hosts join battle*

Count Rabel is a knight of good hardihood, he pricks on his horse with his spurs of fine gold and rides on Torleu the Persian King; neither shield nor hauberk can withstand the blow, and he thrust his golden lance into the King's body, and hurled him dead among the brambles. Thereat the Franks cry: "May the Lord God aid us! Charles has the right, and we must not fail him."

And Guineman sets upon the King of Leutis and shatters his targe adorned with flowers, and thereafter rent asunder his byrnie, and drave all his gonfanon into his body that he fell dead, let whoso will laugh or weep therefor. At this buffet the Franks cry: "Lay on barons, hold not back! Charles has the right against the paynim folk; and the true judgment of God is with us."

Malpramis, on his white charger, drives into the press of the Franks, ever and again striking great blows, that ofttimes he hurls one dead upon another. Baligant speaks first, saying: "Barons, ye whom I have so long nourished, see now my son who goes seeking Charles, and challenging many a baron to the combat; a better vassal I could not wish for. To his rescue now with your lances!" At his words the paynims haste forward, dealing goodly blows that great is the slaughter. Wondrous hard is the battle; never before or after was one so great.

Vast are the hosts and noble the columns; and now all the companies are at battle. The paynims lay on that it is wonder to see. God! but the shaft of many a lance is broken, and shields are shattered, and hauberks unmailed. (Thick lie the maimed and the dead;) lo, the ground is so encumbered with them that the fair grass of the fields which had been green, (is now all reddened with blood.) Yet again the Amiral calls to his followers, saying: "Smite, smite the Christian folk, ye barons." Sore and dread is the battle, that never before or after was one so fierce and so great. Death alone will end it.

Never was battle so great

The Amiral calls to his folk: "Smite, O paynims, for that and nought else have ye come. I will give you women fair and comely, and fiefs and honours and lands." And the paynims make answer: "Yea, it behooves us so to do." And so fierce are their blows they may not recover heir lances, and more than a hundred thousand

swords are drawn. Great and dolourous is the
slaughter. What a battle saw the men who were
there.

The Emperor calls to his Franks, saying:
"Lords and barons, ye are full dear to me, and
in you I set my trust; many a battle have you
won for me, many lands have you conquered, and
many a King dethroned. Right well I know the
guerdon I owe you with my lands and my gold
and my body. Revenge now your brothers and
sons and heirs who yesterday were slain at Roncevals. Well ye know the right is mine against
these paynims." And the Franks make answer:
"Lord, thou sayest truly." Twenty thousand men
Charles has with him, and with one voice they
pledge him their faith that they will not fail him
for any torment or death. There is not one among
them but lays on with his lance, and fiercely they
smite with their swords. Wondrous hard is the
battle.

Malpramis, the baron, rides through the press
doing great slaughter to those of France. But
now Naymes the Duke looks haughtily Malpramis
upon him, and encounters with him like is slain
a man of good hardiness, rends the leather of his
shield, hews off two cantles of his broidered hauberk, and drives his yellow gonfanon into his
body, and hurls him dead to ground among seven
hundred of his comrades.

King Canabeu, the Amiral's brother, spurs on

his horse, and draws his sword, the hilt whereof is set with precious stones, and smites Naymes on his princely helmet, cleaves it in two halves, and with his steel blade cuts through five of its latchets; his steel cap naught avails the Duke, his coif is cut through even to the flesh, and a piece of it falls to the ground. Mighty was the blow, and so astonied thereby is the Duke that he had straightway fallen, an God had not aided him; he clutched the neck of his horse, and if the paynim had dealt him another blow, the noble vassal had been slain straightway. But now Charles of France comes to his succour.

Naymes the Duke is in sore torment, and hastily the paynim makes him ready to strike again. But *Charles slay-* Charles cries to him: "Coward, thy *eth Canabeu* stroke shall cost thee dear!" And he deals him a buffet with all his strength, shatters his shield and breaks it upon his heart, rends asunder the ventail of his hauberk, and hurls him down dead; and his saddle goes empty.

Great is the sorrow of Charles the King when he sees Duke Naymes wounded before him, and his blood flowing out on the green grass. The Emperor saith to him, speaking low: "Fair Sir Naymes, now ride with me. Dead is the felon who brought thee to this strait; once only I set my lance in his body." And the Duke makes answer: "Lord, I believe thee; if I live great honour shall be thine thereby." Then lovingly and loyally they joined company. With them are twenty thousand Franks, and there is not one among them but deals good blows and fights hardily.

The Amiral rides through the press and thrusts upon Count Guineman, breaks his white shield above his heart, rends the sides of his hauberk, and hews off two of his ribs, that he falls dead from his swift horse. Thereafter the Amiral slew Gebuin, and Lorant, and Richard the Old, the liege lord of the Normans; and the paynims cry: "Doughty is Precieuse! Lay on, barons, we have good surety." Many brave knights go down

Would ye might see the knights of Arabia, and those of Occiant and Arguille and Bascle! Well they smite with their lances, dealing stout blows; yet the Franks have no mind to give back, and on both sides many a man is slain. Until evening full sore is the battle; great is the slaughter among the barons of France, and yet more woe will there be or ever the two hosts are disparted.

Both Franks and Arabs deal great blows that lances are shivered, both shafts and bright points. He who saw so many a shield dishonoured, and heard the ring of the bright hauberks and the clash of shield on helm, and saw so many brave knights go down, and heard men cry out as they lay dying upon the ground, must call to mind dolour sore and great. That battle was hard to endure. The Amiral calls upon Apollon, Tervagant and Mahound: "My lords and gods, well have I served you; and I will make you images of fine gold (an ye will succour me against Charles.)" But now Gemalfin, one of those he holds dear, comes before him with ill tidings, saying: "Baligant, lord, misfortune hath come upon you this day; you have lost Malpramis your son, and Canabeu your brother is slain. The victory fell to two of the Franks; of the twain one is the Emperor, methinks, large is he of limb, and looks a mighty lord, and his beard is white as is the flower in April." At the news the Amiral bowed his head, and thereafter hid his face; so great was his grief he thought to die straightway. And he called to him Jangleu of over-sea.

"Come hither, Jangleu," saith the Amiral, "thou art valiant and wise; many a time have I followed thy counsel. What sayest thou now of the Franks and the Arabs, will the victory be with us?" And Jangleu makes answer: "Thou art doomed, Baligant. Thy gods will not save thee. Charles is proud, and his men valiant; never have I seen so warlike a folk. But call ye in the barons of Occiant, the Turks and Enfruns, Arabs and Giants. Do what it behooves you to do and delay not."

Jangleu warneth Baligant

The Amiral has spread out his beard over his hauberk, white it is as is flower on thorn. Come what may he will not skulk from it. He puts a clear trumpet to his lips, and clearly he sounds it that all the paynims hear it, and throughout the field his followers rally. The men of Occiant bray out and neigh, and the men of Arguille yelp like dogs, and they fall upon the Franks with such fury that the stoutest ranks break and give way, and seven thousand fall dead at the one onset.

Count Ogier knew not cowardice, a better warrior never donned hauberk. When he saw the Frankish companies give way, he called Thierry the Duke of Argonne, Geoffrey of Anjou, and Jozeran the Count, and bespoke Charles right proudly: "See now the paynims, how they slay your men! May it please God that ye never more wear crown, an ye do not fight hardily to revenge your shame." No man spoke any word in answer, but they spur on, giving their horses free rein, and smiting the paynims wheresoever they meet them.

Charles the King deals great blows, so likewise do Naymes the Duke, Ogier the Dane, and Geoffrey of Anjou, he who bore the King's standard. Ogier the Dane is full valiant, he pricks on his horse to a gallop, and smites him who holds the Dragon so fiercely that he bears down both the Dragon and the King's ensign. Baligant sees his gonfanon fall and the ensign of Mahound left unguarded, and begins to know that he is in the wrong and the right is with Charles. And the paynims of Arabia begin to weary. The Emperor calls to his Franks: "Tell me now, barons, in God's name, will you aid me?"

The paynims begin to weary

"Thou dost ill to ask it," the Franks make answer: "Base would he be who did not strike hardily."

The day passes and turns towards evening. The Franks and paynims still lay on with their swords. They who arrayed these two hosts were mighty men of battle; and still neither side forgets its war-cry, the Amiral calls aloud Precieuse, and Charles the famous cry Montjoy. Each knows other by his strong voice and clear, and amid the press they met and hurtled together, each dealing great blows with his lance upon the flowered shield of the other, till the spears shiver against the broad bucklers; and they rent apart one another's hauberk, but they did not come at the flesh. Their girths are broken, their saddles thrown back that the two Kings are brought to ground, but swiftly they sprang to their feet, and valiantly they have drawn their swords. This combat cannot be stayed, nor ended save by one man's death.

Precieuse and Mont-joy

Valiant is Charles of fair France, yet the Amiral is neither adread nor dismayed. Both have their bare swords in hand, and each deals other great blows on his shield; they cut through the leather and twofold wood that the nails fall out and the bosses are shattered, then without let or hindrance they strike on their hauberks, and the light springs out from their bright helmets. This combat cannot be staid till one or other cries him in the wrong.

"Bethink thyself, Charles," saith the Amiral, "take counsel and repent thee of thy wrong towards me. Thou hast, as I know, slain my son, and wrongfully hast thou harried my land of Spain; become my man and I will grant it to thee in fee, come and serve me both here and in the East." But Charles makes answer: "That, methinks, were great villainy; I may give neither peace nor love to a paynim. Receive the law which God has made manifest to us, accept Christianity and I will love thee straightway; then believe in the King that wields the world and serve him." "Nay," saith Baligant, "I like not thy sermon." Then they set to again with the swords with which they are girded. *Single combat*

Strong and mighty is the Amiral, he smites Charles upon the helmet of brown steel, breaks and shatters it upon his head, and with his sword carves through the thick hair, and hews off a palm's breadth and more of the flesh, that the bone is left bare. Charles reels and is nigh to falling, but it is not God's will that he be either slain or vanquished; Saint Gabriel hath come to him again, and speaks to him, saying: "What wouldst thou do, great King?"

When Charles heard the blessed voice of the angel he lost all fear and dread of death, and his wit and his strength returned to him. He smites the Amiral with the sword of France, shatters the helmet which shines with *The Franks win the field* precious stones, carves through the skull that the brain runs out, and through all the face even to the white beard, that the Amiral falls dead beyond all help. And Charles cries out Montjoy to summon his men. At his call Duke Naymes comes to him, and seizing Tencendur, helps the King to mount him. The paynims flee; it is not God's will that they abide; and now the prayer of the Franks is granted.

The paynims flee, so the Lord God wills it, and Franks and Emperor pursue after them. Saith the King: "Lords, revenge now your woe. Ease your hearts and your longing, for this morning I saw you weep." And the Franks make answer: "Sire, even so will we do." And every man strikes as many good blows as he may, that few of the paynims escape.

Great is the heat and the dust rises thick; the paynims flee and the Franks press them hard, that the chase lasts even to Saragossa. Bramimonde has mounted her tower; with her are clerks and canons of the false faith never loved of God, unor-
Marsila dies of grief — dained they are, and their heads are untonsured. When the Queen saw the rout of the Arabs she cried aloud: "Help us, O Mahound! Ah gentle King, now are our men vanquished, and the Amiral shamefully slain!" When Marsila heard, he turned him to the wall, and weeping, hid his face. Even so he dies of sorrow; and as he was burdened with sin, eager devils seize upon his soul.

The paynims are slain save some few who flee, and Charles hath won the battle. He has beaten down the gate of Saragossa, well he knows it is no longer defended. He has taken the The taking of Saragossa city and enters therein with his army, and in triumph they lie there that night. Mighty is the King of the hoary beard, and Bramimonde has given over to him the towers, whereof ten are great, and fifty of less size. Well he labours whom the Lord God aids.

The day passes and night darkens, clear is the moon and bright the stars. The Emperor hath taken Saragossa. He commands a thousand Franks that they search the city, the synagogues and the mosques; with axes and mallets of iron they shatter the walls and the idols, till naught is left of their sorcery and their lies. The King believes in God and would do His service; and now the bishops bless the waters, and the paynims are brought to baptism. And if any among them gainsay Charles, he must hang or burn or perish by the sword. More than a hundred thousand are baptized and become true Christians, all save only the Queen; she will be brought a captive to fair France, and it is by love the King would have her converted.

The night passes and the clear day dawns. Charles has stuffed the towers of Sara- The return to France gossa with troops, leaving there a thousand stout knights, who keep the city in the name of the Emperor. The King gets to horse with all his men, and Bramimonde whom he takes with him as a captive; naught but good would he do her. And now in all joy and mirth they turn homewards; in their strength and their might they past Narbonne, and came to the proud city of Bordeaux; and there Charles left the horn of ivory filled with gold and mangons upon the altar of Saint Sevérin the baron, where it may still be seen of pilgrims. Thereafter Charles crossed the Gironde on great ships which he had there, and unto Blaye he bore his nephew, and Oliver, Roland's gentle comrade, and the Archbishop who was both wise and brave; he has the three lords laid in tombs of white marble, in Saint Romain, and there the barons lie even unto this day. The Franks commend them to God and his angels, and Charles rides on over hill and dale; he will make no stay until he comes to Aix, but hastens on till he reaches the entrance stair. And when he is come into his high palace, by messenger he summons his judges, Bavarians and Saxons, men of Lorraine and Friesland, Germans and Burgundians, Poitevins, Normans and Bretons, and the wisest of those of France. And then begins the trial of Ganelon.

The Emperor has returned from Spain, and come again to Aix, the fairest seat in France; he has gone up into his palace and has passed into the hall. To him comes Aude, that fair

damsel, and saith to the King: "Where is Roland, the captain, who pledged him to take me
as his wife?" Thereat Charles is filled
with dolour and grief, he weeps and
plucks his white beard, saying: "Sister, sweet
friend, thou askest me of one who is dead. But
I will make good thy loss to thee, and will give
thee Louis — a better I cannot name — my son he
is, and will hold my marches." "Lord, thy words
are strange to me," Aude makes answer. "May
it not please God or his saints or his angels that
after Roland's death I should yet live." She
loses her colour and falls at the feet of Charles,
and lo, she is dead. God have mercy upon her
soul. The barons of France weep and lament her.

Aude the Fair has gone to her end. But the
King thinks her in a swoon, he is full of pity for
her, and he weeps; he takes her by the hands
and raises her up, but her head falls back upon
her shoulders. When Charles sees that she is
dead, he straightway calls four countesses; Aude
is borne to a convent of nuns hard by, and they
watch by her the night through till dawn. Richly
and fairly they bury her beside an altar, and the
King does her great honour.

The Emperor is come again to Aix. And
Ganelon the felon, in chains of iron, is
in the city, before the palace; serving-
men bound him to a stake, and made fast his
hands with strips of deer's hide; well they beat

Aude la Bele

The trial of Ganelon

him with staves and leathern thongs, for he hath deserved no other bounty. Thus in sore torment he awaits his trial.

It is written in the ancient Geste that Charles did summon men from many lands, and assemble them in the chapel at Aix. Proud is the day and high the festival, that of Saint Silvestre the baron, some men say. And now begins the trial, and ye shall hear of Ganelon who did the treason. The Emperor has commanded that he be brought before him.

"Lords and barons," then saith Charles the King, "now judge me the right concerning Ganelon. He went among my host into Spain with me, and he reft me of twenty thousand of my Franks, and of my nephew whom ye shall see no more, and of Oliver, the courteous, the valiant; and the Twelve Peers likewise he betrayed for money." Then quoth Ganelon: "I were a felon should I deny it. Roland spoiled me of money and goods, for this I sought his death and destruction. But that it was treason I deny." "Now let us take counsel," say the Franks in answer.

He defendeth him of treason

So Ganelon stood before the King; he is strong of body and his face is fresh of hue, if he were true hearted he were a goodly baron. He looks on the men of France, and all the judges, and on his own kin, thirty of whom are with him, and he cries with a loud voice: "For the love of God

now hear me, ye barons! Yea, I was in the host
with the Emperor, and I did him service in all
faith and love. Then Roland, his nephew, con-
ceived a hatred against me, and condemned me
to dolour and death. Messenger I was to King
Marsila, and if I returned unhurt it was by mine
own wit. And I defied Roland the chieftain,
and Oliver, and all their comrades, and this was
heard of Charles and his barons. Revenged me
I have, but in that is no treason." "Let us go
into council," the Franks make answer.

Now that Ganelon sees that his trial is opened,
he calls about him thirty of his kinsmen. One
there is among them to whom all the rest give ear,
and he is Pinabel of the castle of Sorence. Ready
of speech he is, and he can plead full well, and if
it be a question of arms he is a goodly warrior.
Then saith Ganelon: "In you I set my trust;
save me now from calumny and death." "Thou
shalt be saved, and that speedily," saith Pinabel.
"If any Frank condemn thee to hang I will give
him the lie with the point of my sword wheresoever the Emperor shall summon us to do battle
man to man." And Ganelon the Count throws
himself at his kinsman's feet.

Bavarians and Saxons have gone into council
Poitevins and Normans and Franks, and
with them is many a German and Teu-
ton. The men of Auvergne were the
most inclined to grace, and the most friendly

*The barons
incline to
grace*

towards Pinabel. They said one to another: "Best let be. Let us leave the trial, and pray the King that he pardon Ganelon for this time, if he will henceforth serve him in all faith and love. Dead is Roland, ye shall see him no more, nor can ye bring him back with gold or goods; folly it were to hold trial by combat." And there was none who did not agree to this and yea-say it, save only Thierry, the brother of Lord Geoffrey.

The barons return to Charles, and say to the King: "Lord, we beseech you that you pardon Count Ganelon, that henceforth he may serve you in all faith and love. Let him live, for he is of gentle birth. (Roland is dead, never shall ye see him more,) nor will any price restore him to you." "Faithless ye are to me," saith the King in answer.

When Charles sees that they have all failed him, his face and his countenance darken, and "Woe is me!" he cried in his grief. But before

Thierry condemns Ganelon

him is a good knight, Thierry, brother to the Angevin Duke, Geoffrey. Lean he is of body, nimble and slender; blackhaired, and brown of face he is, not tall, and yet not overshort. Courteously he bespeaks the Emperor: "Fair Sir King, make not such sorrow; thou knowest that I have served thee well, and by my lineage I have a right to a share in this trial. Howsoever Roland may have wronged Ganelon thy service should have been his protection; Ganelon is a felon in that he betrayed him, for thereby he has broken his oath to thee and transgressed. And for this I condemn him to hanging and death, and that his body be cast out to the dogs as that of a traitor, since he did traitorously. If he hath any kinsman who will give me the lie, I will uphold my judgment by the sword I have girded here at my side." "That is well said," the Franks make answer.

Then came Pinabel before the King; tall he is, and strong and hardy and swift; short is the term of the man who gets a stroke at his hands. And he saith to the King: "Lord, thine is the quarrel; I pray thee put an end to this clamour. Lo, Thierry has pronounced his judgment, I give him the lie and would do him battle." And he gives him his right *Pinabel gives him the lie* glove made of skin of the deer. Saith the Emperor: "I must have good hostages." Thereupon the thirty kinsmen of Ganelon offer themselves as surety. Then saith the King: "I likewise will give thee pledges; and let these be guarded till the right be made manifest."

When Thierry saw that the battle was toward, he gave Charles his right glove; and the Emperor on his part gave hostages. Then he commanded that four benches be brought into the great square, and thereon they who were to do battle took their places. By the rest the combat was pronounced lawful; and Ogier of Denmark declared the terms. Then the combatants call for their horses and arms.

In that they are near to battle they confess their sins, and are shriven and blessed; they hear mass and receive the communion, and rich offerings they make to the churches. Then the twain come again before Charles. They have fastened on their spurs, and donned their shining hauberks which are both strong and light, made fast upon their heads their bright helmets, and girt on their swords hilted with pure gold, hung their quartered shields about their necks, and now in their right hands they grip their sharp spears, and mount their swift coursers. Thereupon a hundred thousand knights fell a-weeping, for they had pity upon Thierry for Roland's sake. But God knows what the end will be.

Below Aix is a wide meadow, and there the two barons are to do battle. They are men The trial by of good prowess and valour, and their combat horses are swift and keen. The two knights slacken rein, and spurring hard, ride each at other with all the might they have, that their shields are cleft and shattered, their hauberks rent, and thereto their girths are broken that their *saddles turn and fall to earth*. And the hundred thousand men who watch them weep.

Both knights are on the ground, but lightly they spring to their feet. Pinabel is strong and swift and nimble; and each runs upon other, for both now are unhorsed, and with their swords, whereof the pommels are all of gold, they hack and hew their helms of steel; and strong are the blows for the breaking of helms. The Frankish knights make great sorrow; and "O God, make clear the right," cried Charles.

Then saith Pinabel: "Now yield thee, Thierry, and I will be thy man in all love and faith, and of my havings I will give thee whatsoever thou wilt; but do thou make Ganelon's peace with the King." "Nay, that will I not do," quoth Thierry; "I were a very traitor an I should agree. May God judge between thee and me this day."

Quoth Thierry: "Pinabel, thou art a good man of thy hands, tall thou art, and strong, and well fashioned of body, and thy peers ac- Pinabel count well of thy valour; now let be this yieldeth not battle, and I will make thy peace with Charles, but to Ganelon such justice shall be done that men shall not stint talking of it till the world's end." "No, so God help me!" quoth Pinabel. I will hold by my kin, nor will I ever yield me to any man living, rather would I die than bring that shame upon me." Thereupon they began again to strike great blows on their helmets studded with gold and gems, that the fire sprang out towards heaven. By no power may they now be disparted, nor may the combat be ended save by death.

Right valiant is Pinabel of Sorence; he smites Thierry on his helm of Provence, that the fire sprang out therefrom and kindled the grass; he thrusts at him with the point of his sword, cleaves his helmet above his forehead, that the stroke carries to the middle of the face, and the right cheek bursts out a-bleeding; his hauberk is rent down to his belly, but God so guards him that he is not slain.

Thierry sees that he is wounded in the face, and the bright blood flows down upon the grass of the field; he smites Pinabel upon his helm of brown steel, rends it asunder even to the nasal that the brains run out; and he drives the blow home that Pinabel falls dead. So with this stroke the battle is won. And the Franks cry: "God has made manifest his might. It is meet that Ganelon be hung, and likewise his kinsmen, who answered for him."

The right made manifest

When that Thierry had won the battle, Charles the Emperor came to him with four of his barons, Naymes the Duke, Ogier of Denmark, Geoffrey of Anjou and William of Blaye. The King hath taken Thierry in his arms, and dried his face with his great cloak of marten skin, then he throws it down and another is wrapped about him. Thereafter they full gently disarmed the knight, and mounted him upon an Arabian mule; and so he returns again joyously and nobly. They come to Aix and alight in the great square. And now begins the slaying of Ganelon and his kin.

Charles calls his dukes and his counts, saying:

"What counsel ye me concerning those I have in my prison, they who came to the trial to uphold Ganelon, and gave themselves as hostages for Pinabel." And the Franks make answer: "It were ill done an one were let to live." Then the King commands one of his wardens, Basbrun, saying: "Go thou and hang them all to yon blasted tree; by this my beard whereof the hairs are hoary, and if thou let one escape, thou shalt be given over to death and destruction." And Basbrun answered him: "How else should I do?" And by the help of a hundred sergeants he led them away by force; and they were all hung to the number of thirty. For the traitor brings death to both himself and to others.

Thereafter the Bavarians and Germans returned home again, and thereto the Poitevins and Bretons and Normans. Above all the rest the Franks agreed that Ganelon should die by great torture. They let bring four chargers, and then they bind the traitor hand and foot; wild and fleet are the horses, and four sergeants urge them on towards a meadow wherein is a mare. So Ganelon is come to sore punishment, all his sinews are put to the rack, and all his limbs are torn out from his body, and the bright blood flows out on the green grass. Thus Ganelon dies the death of a felon. It is not meet that he who betrays others should boast thereof.

Ganelon's sore punishment

When that the Emperor had done vengeance, he called to him the bishops of France, together with those of Bavaria and Germany, and saith to them: "In my court is a captive, a lady of high parentry, who, having heard many sermons and examples would believe in God, and entreats Christianity. Baptize her that God may receive her soul." And they answer him, saying: "Now for godmothers let there be called four noble dames of good lineage." At the baths of Aix is a great assembly; there they baptize the Queen of Spain, and call her by the name of Juliana. By full knowledge has she become a Christian.

So the Emperor has done justice and appeased his great wrath; and he has brought Bramimonde to Christianity. The day passes and night darkens, and as the King lies in his vaulted chamber, Saint Gabriel comes to him from God, saying: "Charles, now call together the hosts of thy empire, and go in thy might into the land of Bire, and give succour to King Vivien at Imph, for the paynims have laid a siege about his city, and the Christians cry out to thee and entreat thee." Little will had the Emperor to go. "Ah God," he saith, "how is my life oppressed with burdens." And he weeps and plucks his white beard.

Charles summoned to succour Christianity

Here ends the geste which Turoldus tells.

NORMAN KNIGHTS (BAYEUX TAPESTRY)

LIST OF WORDS NOT IN COMMON USE

Almaçur, a title of dignity among the Saracens.

Amiral (the old spelling of admiral), a prince among the Saracens; an emir.

Astonied, (1) confounded, terrified; (2) stunned, as by a blow.

Battle, a division of an army. "The French are bravely in their battles set." Henry V. iv. 4, 69.

Beseen, furnished with, provided with.

Bezant, a gold coin of variable value issued by the Eastern Emperors, and commonly used throughout Western Europe in the middle ages.

Boss, an ornamental projection in the centre of a shield. It was usually of metal, sometimes round in shape, sometimes sharply pointed, and in the *Roland* is often set with precious stones.

Byrnie (Old French brunie), sometimes, apparently, used in the *Roland* synonymously with hauberk to indicate the coat of chain mail; but properly the byrnie was a garment of leather or heavy woven stuff upon which were sewn rings or plates of metal. See the knights from the Bayeux tapestry, page 2.

Bussyne (Old French buisine), a kind of trumpet.

Caitiff, wretched, miserable.

Cantle, a piece, a fragment.

Carbuncle, a deep red gem formerly supposed to give light of itself. See page 95, where carbuncles help to light Baligant's fleet.

Ciclaton, a rich fabric much used in the middle ages for

garments and hangings. It was a kind of silk or bro-
cade, but was sometimes woven with gold. Chaucer's
Sir Thopaz wore a robe " of ciclatoun That costë many a
janë."

Coif, a close-fitting hood of chain mail, attached to the
hauberk, and which so covered the head and face that
only the eyes, nose and mouth were left exposed. See
p. 144.

Dole, sorrow.

Dolour, (1) grief ; (2) pain.

Dromond, a light war vessel.

Embossed (of a shield) provided with a boss or ornamental projection.

The shield, at the end of the eleventh century, was
usually kite-shaped. It was made of wood covered with
leather, painted, gilded, and edged with metal. It was
slightly convex. In the centre was the boss, and from
this bands of iron radiated to the outer edge. The
shields carried by the Normans at the time of the conquest of England were about four feet long, and at the
top, where they were broadest, some twenty inches wide.
The shields were painted in bright colors, sometimes
in simple flat tints, sometimes with geometric patterns,
scrolls, flowers, and strange beasts; hence "the shields
of many devices" of l. 3090 of the *Roland ;* but armo-
rial bearings proper were not introduced till towards
the end of the twelfth century. On the march the
shield was hung about the neck by means of a strap,
called the guige ; when used for defence in battle it was
carried on the forearm, and had for this purpose at its
back, behind the boss, two short straps, called the *enarmes,*
through which the knight thrust his arm to support the
shield. See the Norman shield on p. 144.

Fee, a feud ; land, that is, held of a superior lord in return
for certain services.

Geste, a history. The word first meant exploit, but afterwards came to be used for the chronicle or story in which the exploits were narrated.

Gonfanon, a pennon attached to the shaft of a lance just below the point. See the armed knights, p. 156.

Guige, the strap or band by which the shield was hung about the wearer's neck.

Hauberk, a coat of chain mail reaching to the knee, and provided with a hood or coif for covering the head. It sometimes had a border or fringe, formed by weaving gilded wire into the links of the mail; hence the "broidered hauberks" mentioned in the *Roland*. The "two-fold hauberks" may mean either a hauberk made with double links, or one that has an inner lining of leather or heavy stuff under the mail.

Helm, a cone-shaped casque, or high steel cap, for protecting the head. It was worn over the mail coif, to which it was fastened by means of laces. From the front, downward over the face, extended a projection called the nasal, which covered the nose. For decoration the helm had around its base a circlet which was either carved or set with precious stones. From this there sometimes ran up the height of the cone either two or four bands, also set with jewels. The top was sometimes finished with a ball or knob of metal, but crests did not come into use till later. See cut on p. 144.

Hight, is called, or named.

Hurtle, to dash against, to meet in encounter.

Law, faith.

Mangon, a coin of either gold or silver, the precise value of which is unknown.

Mangonel, an engine of war, used for casting heavy stones.

Mate, to defeat utterly, to confound.

Nasal (of a helmet), the face-guard, or projection which covers the nose.

Paynim (Old French paien) a pagan, a heathen.

Peer, the Twelve Peers, the twelve equals or companions, that is. The list varies in the later *chansons de geste ;* in the *Roland* they are : Roland, Oliver, Ivon, Ivory, Oton, Berenger, Samson, Anseïs, Gerin, Gerier, Engelier, and Gerard de Rousillon.

Quartered (of a shield), divided into four or more parts by the transversal bands which form the framework of the shield.

Stour, tumult, conflict, press of battle.

Valiance, bravery, valor.

Ventail (of a hauberk), that part of the hood of mail which protected the lower part of the face.

Worshipful, worthy of honor.   *Cf.* "a man of worship."

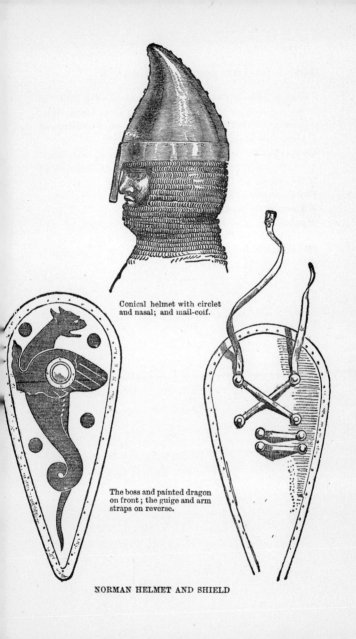

Conical helmet with circlet and nasal; and mail-coif.

The boss and painted dragon on front; the guige and arm straps on reverse.

NORMAN HELMET AND SHIELD

APPENDIX

TRANSLATOR'S NOTE

A PROSE version of a famous poem always requires some apology, or, at least, explanation. In the present instance a successful reproduction in English of the original form, that of the old, decasyllabic, assonanced verse is practically impossible; for assonance, almost a lost art, could hardly be revived in a poem of some four thousand lines. On the other hand, any modern English metre, either a rhyming measure with its regular beat and recurring consonantal sounds, or blank verse with its memories of "proud full sail," or ordered stateliness, not only changes the character of the poem, — as any change of form must of necessity, — but also fixes the attention upon an elaborate medium, as the original does not. True, the original, in old France, had its background of chant and viol, but this background was more extrinsic than any setting of modern metre can be. Stripped of this background or accompaniment, as on the printed page it is to-day, the narrative comes to us with singular simplicity and directness; and I know of no equally famous poem in which, to the same degree, the story, and not the telling of it, is the thing. The only decoration lies in the recurring epithet and in epic repetition; and this simplicity — bareness even — of the style, with its swiftness and downrightness of narration, can, it has seemed to me, be best rendered to-day in prose.

In the style I have tried to keep at least something of the memory of yesterday. Certain of Malory's knightly words and phrases I have allowed myself, but Malory's manner, colored and various, is not that of " Roland," and in reading the "Morte d'Arthur" I have tried not to forget the barer narrative of " Maccabees."

The translation follows closely Müller's text: "La Chanson de Roland nach der Oxforder Handscrift," herausgegeben von Theodor Müller. Third edition, Göttingen, 1878. In only a few instances have I adopted readings suggested by M. Gaston Paris or M. Petit de Julleville. These instances are indicated in the text by italics.

The parentheses enclosing certain sentences or clauses indicate lines which do not occur in the Oxford Manuscript, but which, based on the comparison of other manuscripts, have been inserted in the text by Müller to fill obvious gaps in the sense. No attempt, however, has been made to indicate his emendations in the case of single words or phrases. The longer passages in square brackets are from the Venetian Manuscript; quoted by Müller in his notes, they are here in-

serted in the text by the translator at those points where a fuller narrative is needed for the clearness of the story.

The old division of the *laisses*, or irregular stanzas, — each complete in itself, and forming a little scene quite separate from its fellows, — has seemed to me at once too interesting and too structural to be given up. I have therefore followed it closely in my paragraphs. After much hesitation, I have also followed the original in its sudden shifts of tense, and almost constant use of the present. At only the dullest moments does the narrator by the use of the preterite remind his hearers that he is telling over a long-ago story; as soon as he comes to action, or even to the description of a scene, he steps straightway into the present. And contrary as this use is to the custom of English narrative, I have ventured to keep it, thinking it akin to the sudden changes into direct discourse and constant use of dialogue, and that both together help to give us the attitude of the trouvère.

The spelling of the proper names also requires a word of explanation. Since the book is to be used in schools I have tried to do away with all unnecessary difficulties in the text. To this end I have given familiar names, whether geographical or personal, the form familiar to the English reader; thus I have written Geoffrey of Anjou and Saint Michael, Bordeaux and Apulia, instead of

Geifreit and Michiel, Burdele and Puille. But in the case of unfamiliar names, whether of the lesser personages in the story, or of imaginary geographical places, I have — thinking that nothing was gained in ease by the use of modern French — given the form of the name as it occurs in the oblique case in the Old French; and thus have written Malbien, not Maubien, and Haltilie, not Hautile.

One exception, however, I have made in the case of the Old French *un* that becomes in modern French *on*, and I have, both for euphony and outward uniformity, always, even in the case of unfamiliar names, given the modern form; for in the case of so common a termination it is hard to write Samson, Guyon, and Narbonne, and not to write also Nivelon, Besgon, and Blandonne.

Obviously, it is impossible to follow a double system and not to fall into difficulties in special instances, and I must pray the reader's pardon if my division of the familiar and unfamiliar has not always been his. In some instances I have been guided by fitness; when, for instance, a familiar, translatable name occurs coupled with an untranslatable one, I have, for the sake of uniformity, given to both the Old French form, and have written, not Walter, but Gualter del Hum. Again, in the case of Apollo, I have made an exception for the sake of connotation, and I have retained the old form Apollon, as having in it

less of the sun and more of the fierce god of the
paynims. Connotation again, and something of
taste, underlies the choice of the form Aude;
mere personal taste the choice of Roncevals among
its many variants, and of Charles and Marsila.
Though in modern history the Frankish emperor
is to-day always Karl, he may, I think, still be
Charles in literature. The Old French Marsilie
seemed to me too hard a form for a name that
occurs so often in the text, and of the various
forms given to the name in other English versions of the story, Marsilius, Marsile, and Marsila,
I have preferred the last as coming more easily
to the tongue.

One other liberty I have taken, and when the
same name occurs for two or more persons I have,
for the convenience of the reader, given the names
slightly different forms. Thus, of the three
Otons, I call the first, who was one of the Twelve
Peers, Oton; the second, the marquis who fig-
ures in the third part of the story, Odo; and
the third, Odo's vassal, Otto. Of the two Malprimes I have called the first, Marsila's nephew,
Malprimes; and the second, Baligant's son, Malpramis.[1]

The translator is, of course, as little commen
tator as editor. The few notes aim only to give

---

[1] This is the form actually used for Baligant's son in the
Oxford MS., but for the sake of the verse it is, in modern editions, always changed to Malprimes.

in a form convenient for use in the classroom a slight summary of the historical comment current in the modern French editions, so far as that comment really adds to the understanding of the story. In both the preparation of the notes and introduction, and in the revision of the translation, I have been much indebted to the translation, notes, and prefaces of M. Petit de Julleville; to the glossary, notes, and prefaces of M. Gautier's nineteenth edition, and to those of M. Gaston Paris in his "Extraits de Roland;" also to the many notes, reviews, and essays on the "Roland" that have appeared in the "Romania." The notes on armor are mainly drawn from Viollet-le-Duc's "Dictionnaire du Mobilier Français" and J. Hewitt's "Ancient Armor and Weapons in Europe," London, 1860.

I. B.

November, 1903.

NOTES

Page 1. — "but serves **Mahound**, and **worships Apollon**." In the *chansons de geste* the Saracens are always represented as polytheists; and the three gods most commonly ascribed to them are Apollon, Tervagant and Mahound. The origin of Tervagant, or Termagant — the form in which the name usually occurred in English — is unknown. Apollon, or Apolin, is the god Apollo, the final *n* being but the termination of the oblique case. But just as Mahound is reduced to a mere idol (see p. 94) so, too, Apollo appears stripped of all his proper attributes; for to the mediæval story-teller it was a point of honor not to be too familiar with strange gods.

Page 4. **Mangonels.** The Old French word in the text is *cadable*, an engine for throwing stones, the name of which never found its way into English.

Page 4. **Cordova,** so the old French name Cordres is usually taken. Probably the trouvère knew only a few Spanish names and used them at hazard. Cordova was to him a rich city in Spain, not a dot on the map; it is evident he thinks of it as in the north, at no great distance from Saragossa.

Page 6. **Saint Michael of the Peril,** "of the sea" being understood. *In periculo maris* was the name under which was dedicated the monastery of Mont Saint Michel, founded in the ninth century on the border of Normandy and Brittany. The frequency with which the name occurs in the *Roland* has sometimes been taken as a proof that the poet knew the monastery well. M. Gautier would have him a native of Avranches in Normandy ; M. Gaston Paris sees in the reference only a trace of the Breton origin of the story.

Page 8. **Roland's conquests.** Although in the beginning of the poem Charles is said to have conquered all Spain, it is clear that for the trouvère Spain ends with the Ebro. All the action of the story takes place between the Pyrenees and Saragossa. Of the towns here named as conquered by Roland, Pina, Tudela, Balaguer and Valtierra are all in this region. Noples, Commibles and Sezilie are unidentified ; but judging from other *chansons de geste* in which the story of their capture is told, Noples and Commibles seem to be near the Pyrenees. If a southern town is mentioned in the story, as, for instance, Cordova, it is thought of as being in the north.

Page 9. — **"give me now the glove and the staff."** M. Petit de Julleville in his edition of *Roland*, p. 407, notes that : "The glove and the staff were the symbols of investiture whether it were a question of a fief, an office, or, as in the present instance, of an embassage. 'The glove especially was constantly used as a symbol in the middle ages. A man brought accusation against another, or challenged him to combat, by throwing down his glove. To throw your glove was provocation ; to give it was a sign of submission.'" See p. 87, where Roland, to show his absolute submission, offers his glove to God, and p. 102, where Marsila, as a sign that he renounces his fief, gives his glove to Baligant.

Page 10. **The Twelve Peers,** that is, the twelve equals or companions. Here it is a question of a military brotherhood. The historical institution of the twelve peers of France was established much later.

Page 10. **Then said the King : "Ganelon, come thou hither."** Throughout the following passage, ll. 280–341 (p. 10 to foot of p. 12), I have followed Müller's reärrangement of the order of the Oxford MS.

Page 12. — "**lo, I stand before thee, ready to do thy commandment.**" Here some lines seem to have been omitted in the Oxford MS. One expects Charles to give Ganelon the message which he is to take to Marsila. In the later redactions of the poem we find a *laisse* giving in full all that Ganelon says on pp. 16 and 17 (ll. 431–37 and ll. 469–83) ; and this passage is inserted in most modern editions. In its favour we have the epic convention of repeating messages word for word. But one would like to think that Ganelon distorts his message to provoke Marsila. There is no mention elsewhere in the poem of half Spain being given as a fief to Roland, though, had it been part of the compact proposed by Charles, one would expect some reference to it on Ganelon's return from Saragossa.

Page 21. **The Great Land** (Terre Majur in the text) signifies Charlemagne's empire as a whole.

Page 26. In mediæval literature coming events are constantly foreshadowed by dreams. The end of the poem explains the meaning of Charlemagne's visions. The bear signifies Ganelon ; the right arm of Charles, Roland ; the leopard typifies Ganelon's kinsman, Pinabel ; and the greyhound, Thierry of Anjou, who does battle with Pinabel for Charlemagne. *Cf.* King Arthur's dream of the serpents and his vision of Sir Gawain in book xxi. of the *Morte d'Arthur.*

Page 27. — "**wrathfully he turns to his step-father.**" This laisse, so different in tone from the preceding, is thought to be either from some different version of the story, or to have been added by the fancy of a dull scribe. There is no trace of it in the Venetian MS.

Page 32. **Roncevals,** the modern Spanish Roncevalles, is in the Western Pyrenees, on the road from Pamplona to Saint Jean-Pied-de-Port, about seven miles from the French frontier. Eginhard, in his account of the loss of the rearguard, does not specify the name of the valley in which the defeat occurred ; but a very early and consistent tradition connects the battle with Roncevalles.

Page 33. The origin and history of Roland's sword Durendal is very variously given in the *chansons de geste.* Several accounts, however, agree in making it the work of that forger of so many of the weapons of mediæval romance — Weland the Smith. According to the *Karlamagnus Saga* it was one of three famous swords — the other two being Turpin's Almace and Ogier's Courtain — given to Charlemagne by Malabin d' Ivon the Jew, as a ransom for his father.

Page 42. — **Montjoy,** the old war-cry of France. I have used this form of the word as being the most familiar, although for the *Roland* Monjoie would be more correct. See the account of the origin of the name given on pp. 91–2. The real origin of the word is unknown.

Page 66. — " **Aforetime he took Noples against thy commandment.**" Other *chansons de geste* explain the reference. The *Karlamagnus Saga* begins with the capture of Noples, but gives a somewhat different version of the story. According to that, Roland and Oliver took Noples on the express command of Charles; but they put to death its king, Fouré, whom they had been bidden to spare, and tried afterwards to wash away the blood that their act might not be discovered.

Page 75. Nothing is known of the story of Droön and Maëlgut; probably it was told in one of the *chansons de geste* which has not come down to us.

Page 81. After "for upholding and counselling the good" I omit line 2213, *E pur glutuns e veintre e esmaier,* which is evidently a mere scribal repetition of line 2211, *pur orguillus e veintre e esmaier.*

Page 111. — " **St. Peter's ensign it was.**" The pope did actually give Charlemagne a banner as a symbol of empire. Here this old Carlovingian banner is confused with the oriflamme of the Capetians, but, in fact, there was no connection between them.

Page 115. Just as Charles is made the chief of all

Christendom, so Baligant is the leader of all Paynimry. M. Gaston Paris, in *La Romania*, ii. p. 330, discusses the peoples of Baligant's army. Part of these are real and historic; others, as the Gros and the men of Joi and Maruse, are either imaginary, or have not yet been identified. It is noteworthy that the historic peoples are not those with whom Christian Europe came in contact at the time of the Crusades, but those with whom they fought along the eastern borders of Europe in the ninth, tenth, and eleventh centuries. They fall, for the most part, into two great families — the Slavs and the Tartars. To the Tartars belong the Huns, the Hungarians, the Avars, and the Pincenati, a savage wandering tribe that lived on the borders of the Black Sea, and were the terror of pilgrims in the tenth and eleventh centuries. Among the Slavs are the Lutici, or Wilzi, and Sorbi, who lived along the upper Elbe; the Prussians, the Lechs, the Russians and the Milciani.

Page 130. **Narbonne** is quite off the road from Saragossa to Bordeaux. But other versions of the story give us a long account of the capture of Narbonne by the Franks on their return from Spain; probably the trouvère knew this story, and did not know the map of France.

Page 130. From the twelfth century on, Roland's tomb at Blaye was famous. Even in the sixteenth century it was visited by Francis I. In the next century the church was burned. M. Camille Jullian (*Romania*, xxv. p. 169) points out the importance of Blaye at the time the legend of Roland was growing up. Situated on the old Roman road that crossed France from Spain to the Rhine, it was a natural stopping-place for travellers going north or south; it was also famous for the shrine of Saint Romain. Near its church was a group of the nameless tombs of the early Christians; these popular imagination ascribed to various famous persons, as Roland and Oliver.

Page 132. — **"Roland spoiled me of money and goods."** This passage clearly does not fit the story, and is usually taken as corrupt. Ganelon's second defence of himself (p. 133) was a legitimate one at a time when private warfare was accounted lawful. Having defied Roland before witnesses he was free to make war upon him.

Page 140. Nothing is known to-day of Bire or the city of Imph, or of King Vivien; but the story was undoubtedly told in some *chanson de geste* that has not come down to us. So here the trouvère connects his story with the Carlovingian cycle, and makes it one of a great series telling of the old warfare of Christian and heathen.

Page 140. — "**Here ends the geste that Turoldus tells.**" A much discussed line that does not help us to the authorship of the poem. Génin, one of the early editors of the *Roland*, attempted to identify this Turoldus with the Thérould to whom William the Conqueror gave the Abbey of Malmesbury in 1069. But this theory has been given up, and even the meaning of the line is held as doubtful. It may refer to the minstrel who sang the story, or even to the scribe who wrote it down, instead of to the poet who composed it.

ARMED KNIGHTS WITH LANCES AND GONFANONS

here this morning. Off to Gretna, I figured, by the looks of them, and in a hurry."

"How long ago?" Isabel pushed the money toward the woman, who scooped it up and slid it into her pocket.

"Three hours or more," the woman said, moving back toward the door. At Isabel's stricken look, she added, "Headed north, for sure. I don't collect they'll get farther than Northampton tonight. Might have heard 'em say so, in fact." The woman bobbed her head and slipped out of the little parlor.

Three hours. Although she longed to sit quietly for a few more minutes, Isabel knew that time was critical to finding Julia and Chiswick before irreparable damage was done. Setting down her cup, she sent to the kitchen, where Willington was just finishing her own tea.

It was after midnight when Isabel's coach arrived at the Angel in Northampton. Isabel did not leave the carriage but sent the footman to inquire about anyone who had arrived that day. The negative answer sent them next to the George.

By the time they pulled up in front of the Rose and Crown, Isabel had begun to lose heart. When the footman returned to report that a Mr. Chesterton and his sister had taken rooms for the night, Isabel breathed a sigh of relief and sent him back to tell the landlord she wanted to speak with him.

Willington was wide awake and wide-eyed in her corner of the carriage. Isabel could tell she was perishing to talk about Julia's flight and their pursuit. But Isabel did not broach that or any subject. This was between her and Julia. She only thanked God that Chiswick and Julia were in separate rooms. And she suspected she knew whose money had paid for that extravagance.

Isabel leaned her head back against the soft leather of the seat and let her eyes fall shut. It had been a long and grueling trip. She was exhausted and slightly ill. Her head swam with fatigue, and she'd had an annoying stitch in her side for the past two hours. She longed only to stretch out on a clean bed and sleep.

The footman roused her with news that the landlord awaited her. Accepting the footman's help descending from the carriage, Isabel sent Willington to see if she could find some refreshment and her coachman off to take care of the horses.

The innkeeper stood, bleary-eyed and hastily dressed, in the narrow entry hall. He was irritable at having been awakened and in no mood to be helpful.

"Gentleman paid for the room. Paid for his privacy. I'm not letting you barge in there and disturb his sleep." The innkeeper leaned against a rough plastered wall and scratched his arm.

Isabel shuddered. She hoped whatever was making him itch was confined to his own quarters.

"This is very important. I have . . . important news for Mr. Chesterton that he will be very glad to hear." Isabel stretched her neck, trying to ease the tension in her shoulders.

The man looked unconvinced. "He's a paying guest."

Isabel cast about for a persuasive argument. She lowered her eyes and was confronted by the sight of the innkeeper's bare feet. Distracted, she lost her train of thought.

"I've got to get back to my bed." The innkeeper was obviously growing impatient.

"Oh." Isabel's hand moved to her back. The carriage ride had played havoc with her body. Everything was cramped and tense.

"Ma'am?"

Isabel waved a hand. "It's nothing. You were saying?"

"I were saying that the man's a *paying* customer."

The fog cleared, and Isabel finally grasped what the innkeeper was trying to tell her. "Of course. Foolish of me." She opened her reticule and placed some money on the man's extended palm. "Will that be sufficient?"

The innkeeper closed his fist around the coins. "Number seven. Top of the stairs." He turned and stalked toward the back of the inn.

The stairwell was dark, and the first-floor hallway was darker still. Isabel could see light from a room at the end of corridor and hoped it was Willington lighting the way to a cup of tea when she was done with the odious business on which she was bound.

Number seven was, indeed, right at the top of the stairs. Isabel tried the latch. The door was locked. Of course. Only a fool would leave the door to a room such as this unlocked. Chiswick might be a rogue, but he was not a complete fool. Isabel lifted her hand and knocked. No response. She knocked again. Dead silence.

Gathering her courage, Isabel pounded on the door until she heard a muffled sound from within and then Chiswick's voice. "What is it?"

"Open the door this minute, or I shall have it broken down." Isabel kept her voice low, but its steely resolve seemed to penetrate the wood. She heard the latch snick, and the door cracked open.

"Let me in." She put her foot against the door and pushed.

"Isabel?" Chiswick stepped back. He looked as though he had pulled on his trousers under his nightshirt, but Isabel could not be sure. The room was lit only by the sliver of moon still visible in the sky.

She shut the door. "Give me some light."

Chiswick fumbled on the table and finally struck a light to a lopsided branch of candles sitting by the low bed.

"What are you doing here?" he asked.

"What in the name of all that's holy do you think I'm doing here, you lackwit?" Isabel marched into the room and glared at Chiswick. Despite his unshaven face and unkempt hair, he was still a handsome man. Isabel could understand Julia's infatuation.

Sense seemed to finally penetrate Chiswick's sleep-addled brain. "Julia."

Isabel scowled. "Julia," she said, her voice hard, her jaw set.

Chiswick ran his hands through his hair and walked toward the portmanteau sitting open on a straight-backed chair near the window. "Let me make myself presentable."

"Stay where you are. You don't need to be presentable for this discussion."

Chiswick stopped dead and turned back to Isabel. "Very well, I have run off with the earl's sister. We've been here all night. It's too late."

"It's not too late. I will take her out of here, and no one will know."

Chiswick's sensual lips twisted into a sneer. "Oh, someone will know. I will know."

"What do you want?" Isabel knew that the answer was money. But she did not know how much it would cost to buy off this cad.

"You know what I want, Isabel. The only thing that has changed is the woman."

"She is but a girl, George. Let me take her home." Isabel felt drained, but she would fight for Julia if she must.

"Relinquish an earl's sister? For how much?"

"Five hundred pounds." Isabel pulled a figure out of the air.

Chiswick laughed. "Lady Julia Chamberlayne is worth a deal more than that."

"Do not fence with me. Name your terms." Isabel

pushed the portmanteau off the chair and slumped onto the seat.

"Ten thousand." Chiswick's expression dared Isabel to say she would not pay that for Julia.

"Ten thousand, then, as soon as we return to London."

"How great a fool do you think me?" Chiswick moved closer to where Isabel sat, until he was towering over her.

Isabel stood, forcing Chiswick to step back. "I did not bring ten thousand pounds with me. How great a fool do you think *me?*"

"Bring it then, and I'll give you the girl."

A potent mix of anger and panic spiked through Isabel. She dug her fingernails into her palms, searching within herself for calm. Hasty action would only make this horrible business worse.

She closed her eyes, fatigue and despair overtaking anger. "Keep me with you, then. I will send for the money. Eloping with Julia will bring you nothing but trouble. Haddon will never give her a dowry if she's married a fortune hunter over the anvil."

Chiswick did not speak, but Isabel knew that he was considering her suggestion.

"It is your best option," she said, holding out her hand palm up, making the offer tangible.

Chiswick nodded once. "I suppose it is, if what you say is true."

"I'll just go wake Julia and send her home in my coach." Isabel stepped back toward the door.

"No." In a single stride, Chiswick was beside her, his hand firmly against the door.

"But . . ." What did the man want now?

"I will fetch Lady Julia. There will be no private communication between you." He wrenched open the door and was through it before Isabel could speak.

Isabel pursued Chiswick into the darkened hallway.

Ignoring the nagging pain in her back, she grabbed his arm before he could reach for the latch on the door he was facing. "You do not intend to enter without knocking?"

"Naturally not." Chiswick frowned and raised his hand to rap on the door. He waited several seconds and knocked harder.

Isabel heard the sounds of movement in the room and stepped closer to call through the door. "Julia. It's Isabel."

After some scraping and shuffling, the door cracked open and Julia appeared, fully clothed and holding a candle. "Isabel?"

"Let me in." Isabel pushed against the door, and Julia stepped back.

Before Isabel crossed the threshold, Chiswick shoved past her and strode to the middle of the room. Isabel followed, then closed the door and glanced around. Although hardly elegant, the room was tidy and at least smelled clean. And the bed had not been disturbed. She breathed a small sigh of relief.

Julia stood in the middle of the room looking perturbed as Isabel lit another candle. "What is going on?"

"Er . . ." Chiswick shrugged and glanced toward Isabel.

"You are going home," Isabel said, moving toward the bed and pulling out the valise that stood open at its foot.

"I am not." Julia crossed the room and yanked the valise out of Isabel's hand, pushing it behind her.

A wave of nausea passed over Isabel and she dropped to the bed, sitting for a moment with her head in her hands. Inhaling deeply, she looked up at the girl standing before her, hands on her hips, long brown hair cascading over her shoulders in deep waves. She looked so young and innocent. If only Isabel could prevent her from making a dreadful mistake.

"You must," she said, finally. "You must return to London before anyone knows you've gone. Please, please trust me."

"Do as she says." Chiswick's insinuating voice sounded from the far corner of the room.

"What?" Julia spun around to face Chiswick.

"Go home. You are not wanted here."

From where she sat, Isabel could sense Julia's confusion deepen. She didn't move, waiting to let Chiswick's words find their mark.

Julia stood motionless for seconds, simply staring at Chiswick.

Isabel pushed herself up off the bed. Approaching Julia, she put her arm around her shoulders and drew her back. "It is for the best," she whispered, turning the girl toward her valise. "Pack your things. My coach is outside."

Her eyes brimming, Julia shook her head. "You cannot force me to leave George. I love him."

"But I do not love you, my dear. Mrs. Chamberlayne is much more my style." Chiswick's voice issued from the corner where he still stood, arms crossed over his chest.

Color drained from Julia's face as she turned to stare at Isabel. "You?" she whispered, her voice registering the betrayal.

"Go home." Isabel said nothing more. What more was there to be said? The only thing she could do now was get Julia out of here and, if possible, have a moment alone with Willington or her coachman before they all departed for London.

Chiswick seated himself on the only comfortable chair in the room and crossed one leg over the other as he watched the ladies repack Julia's bag. Isabel was conscious of his avid gaze but more aware of the tears now coursing down Julia's cheeks.

Her hand brushed Julia's as they both reached into the valise. Isabel let fall the chemise she was holding and grasped the young girl's hand. "Please trust me," she said softly.

Julia yanked her hand away.

"What's that you're saying?" Chiswick asked, leaving his chair to stand by the two women.

"I must fetch Willington to accompany Julia back to London." Isabel dropped the silver-backed hairbrush she had just picked up into the bag and moved toward the door.

"I think not." Chiswick intercepted her. "Where is she?"

"I—I'm not sure." Isabel was certain that if she were not ill and exhausted from the carriage ride, she would have been able to think of a way to speak to Willington without Chiswick overhearing. Now, all she could do was stand stupidly with her hand on the latch.

Chiswick knocked her hand away and replaced it with his own. "I will find her, then. Come with me."

Isabel didn't move. "I will stay with Julia."

"Oh, no, you won't. Julia will wait while we go together to fetch this elusive maid." Chiswick took Isabel by the wrist and released the latch.

There had been no need for the foolish argument. When Chiswick finally threw open the door, they found Willington hovering in the hallway.

"Is this your maid?"

When Isabel nodded, he dropped her wrist and gestured to the woman to enter the room.

Events were spinning away from her. Willington's arrival marked one less opportunity to get a message to Sidney. Isabel's heart pounded as she contemplated the possible outcome of her situation. Quietly, she reached out and took Julia's hands.

Julia pulled away from her. "Don't touch me. You have ruined all my hopes of happiness."

Isabel glanced toward Chiswick. He was listening to every word. She would not be able to say anything to purpose. She shifted her attention back to her young sister-in law. "I only hope you will understand one day soon."

Julia shrugged. "I understand now. Sidney will hear all about this . . . this betrayal. You will never be able to show your face in London again."

"Oh—" Isabel's hand flew to her side, and she sat heavily on the bed.

Julia looked straight ahead, her gaze fixed on the closed door. "Indeed. How could you deceive both me and my brother in this way? It is infamous."

Argument was impossible and hope was steadily dwindling. Isabel kept her eyes on her maid, willing her to grasp what was happening, to comprehend that the rescue of Julia had created a new problem, to have the presence of mind to tell someone who would act.

Willington had been viewing the activity in the room with an air of distress. "What am I to do, Mrs. Chamberlayne?"

"Accompany Lady Julia to Bruton Place and explain *everything* to my aunt."

"But madam . . ."

"No more talk." Chiswick gestured toward the maid.

"Do it." Isabel prayed Willington would know what it was she should do.

Julia took her valise and stalked to the door, her face set in a mask of misery.

Isabel started to rise from the bed but was forestalled by a gesture from Chiswick.

He shook his head. "No. I'll see them off. You stay here."

Isabel stayed, too tired and too sick to do anything else. As Chiswick ushered Julia and Willington from the room, Isabel prayed that her maid had understood or that Julia would tell Sidney exactly what she had seen. She prayed that Sidney would trust her, and she prayed that she would survive this foolhardy rescue. Wrapping her arms around herself, she collapsed back on the bed.

Chapter 23

The Dover road had seen its share of traffic in this season of victory. And much of it was far more illustrious than Sidney Chamberlayne, former major in the Light Dragoons. But none of it was more worried.

The sun was out, but the air was cool, promising the onset of autumn. A good day to ride. Sidney put his head down and urged Chiron to greater effort. They had stopped one night on the road, to allow the great chestnut time to regain his stamina, but Sidney was determined to reach London before another night passed. The more he thought about it, the more likely it seemed that George Chiswick was the man he sought. There were so many tiny clues that he had overlooked in the social and emotional maelstrom that had followed his marriage.

Isabel had made it clear that Chiswick was a fortune hunter and had done so on more than one occasion. Why had it only just occurred to Sidney that a man in tightened circumstances might be seeking a fortune through other, less acceptable, avenues than marriage? He cursed softly. His mind had been so full of Isabel and his perceived duty that all he could see of Chiswick was that he had once been Isabel's suitor. Sidney wondered if perhaps he was not cut out to be anything but a soldier after all.

London loomed in the distance, and Sidney could

feel Chiron's stride lengthen. They both longed to reach home. When he left Dover, Sidney had thought he would go immediately to Whitehall on arrival. But the closer they got to the city, the stronger the pull toward Bruton Place, toward Isabel. If she had not captured his heart, she had quite firmly lodged herself in his imagination.

Sidney rounded the corner from Berkley Square into the midst of a commotion. Isabel's carriage, covered with mud, stood at the front door as servants streamed from the house, opening the doors, assisting the coachman from his box, and all speaking at once. He could hardly credit that Isabel would countenance such unseemly behavior.

The carriage door hung open as if someone had just left it, and Isabel's maid stepped out. She looked as though she had been dragged behind the carriage for several miles. Her gown was soiled and wrinkled, and her eyes were heavily shadowed. She peered around in a disoriented fashion and finally hurried up the granite steps into the house.

What had happened? Where was Isabel? Sidney signaled a groom who was part of the group milling around the carriage with no real purpose.

"What is going on here?" Sidney dismounted and stood beside his sweating horse, gently rubbing the beast's nose.

"Don't know, sir." The boy pulled his forelock, keeping his head bent low.

Sidney's impatience flared. "Take my horse and see that he is well cared for. He has had a hard ride. Now go."

The boy bobbed his head and led the big chestnut off, leaving Sidney to contemplate the rest of the crowd clustering near the carriage.

"Take these horses and the carriage to the mews, and take yourselves to your occupations." Sidney's steely voice overrode the muttering of the servants. It was the voice he used in command, and it had the desired effect.

Turning his back on the dispersing crowd, Sidney took the steps two at a time and entered the house, slamming the door behind him. In the entryway, he found yet more chaos.

It seemed as though all the servants who were not out on the street were gathered in the front hall. Most of them hung back against the walls, but two of the maids fluttered around Isabel's maid, who was looking even paler than she had when she left the carriage. Several were hauling in trunks that had been unloaded from the coach, and one, whom he thought worked at Haddon House, was trying to hand a vinaigrette to his sister.

"Julia!" His voice brought sudden quiet to the previously noisy crowd.

Julia looked up at him, her eyes red and puffy and her expression distraught. Sidney looked around at the rest of the group. Where was Isabel? Where was Lady Louisa?

"Get out, all of you," he said in a tone so deadly calm that the hallway cleared immediately.

"Oh, Sidney." Julia gulped as tears sprang to her eyes.

"Not in the hallway." Sidney put an arm around his sister and led her to the family drawing room. He sat her on a settee, pulled out his handkerchief and returned to the door.

"Find Mrs. Chamberlayne," he said to the first footman he encountered.

The footman all but saluted. "Mrs. Chamberlayne is not at home, sir. Shall I fetch Lady Louisa?"

"Yes, I suppose you had better do that. And quickly." Sidney closed the door in the man's face and returned to his sister.

"You . . . you won't find Isabel." Julia sniffed into the handkerchief Sidney had given her. "You'll never see her again."

Sidney's breath seized. He took Julia by the shoulders and gave her a shake. "What? What do you mean I'll never see Isabel again? What has happened to her? Is she . . . is she hurt?"

Julia shook her head and blew her nose loudly. "No. She's not hurt. Not that conniving, faithless, horrible—"

"You are speaking about my wife and your sister." Sidney's firm voice stopped Julia in midsentence.

"Your wife has run off with Mr. Chiswick," Julia said and then burst into a fresh storm of tears.

The back of Sidney's neck turned to ice. Every muscle became rigid, and his vision narrowed. Julia winced, and Sidney very carefully released the iron grip he still had on her arms.

"What are you talking about?"

Julia sniffled and rubbed at her arms. "Isabel has run off with Chiswick," she said again, her face locked in a stubborn frown.

"Ridiculous." Sidney took a deep breath and stood up. He paced to the fireplace and back without looking at Julia. The idea was preposterous. Isabel may have had a lively past, but she would not run off with a fortune hunter.

"It is not," Julia said, drawing his attention back to her. "I saw them."

At that moment the door opened and Lady Louisa came bustling in, trailed by Isabel's maid. "Sidney."

Sidney walked over to her and kissed her cheek. "My sister insists Isabel has run away with George Chiswick," he said, trying to keep his tone light.

Lady Louisa nodded.

"Surely you don't believe this?"

Louisa ignored him and turned toward Julia, reaching out a wrinkled hand to push stray hairs off the girl's forehead. Only at that moment did Sidney recognize how disheveled his sister was. Her clothes, like Isabel's maid's, looked as though they had been slept in, and her hair had obviously been hastily pinned up in an amateurish fashion.

Sidney watched as Lady Louisa subjected Julia to a similar examination. The older woman's face registered Julia's unkempt state and tearstained face. She pulled out her own lace-trimmed handkerchief and placed it in Julia's hand, removing the one that Sidney had given her earlier.

Lady Louisa finally turned back to Sidney. "Willington tells the same story, but she is under the impression that Isabel did not stay willingly."

"She was with him and she was willing. I told him." Julia pointed at Sidney. "No one will believe me."

"I believe you saw Isabel and Chiswick," Louisa said.

"Well, good." Julia sat back and examined the handkerchief that lay crumpled in her hand.

"Willington says you left them in Northampton." Lady Louisa held Julia's gaze until the girl nodded.

"Northampton?" Sidney exploded out of his chair.

Lady Louisa patted Julia's arm and gave her a little push. "Go to your room and have Benson send for some food and a tisane."

"No. I want Sidney to know everything." Julia crossed her arms across her chest and glared at Lady Louisa.

"I promise you, he will, but first you need some rest. Go. You go, too." Louisa nodded at the maid.

"What is going on?" The minute the door shut behind Julia and Willington, Sidney closed in on Lady Louisa. His temper held only by the thinnest thread, he barely prevented himself from tearing the room apart.

Before she answered, Lady Louisa crossed the

room, poured a large portion of brandy into a sparkling crystal glass and handed it to Sidney.

"Don't bite my head off," she said and then proceeded to relate the full story of Julia's elopement and Isabel's pursuit, including Willington's surmise that Isabel had exchanged herself for Julia in order to get Chiswick to let the girl return.

Isabel rolled onto her side and wrapped her arms over her stomach. The pain was excruciating. She no longer believed her cramps were the result of stiffened muscles, nor, much as she wanted to, could she convince herself that she had eaten something that made her ill. The pain was about the baby.

Almost as soon as she admitted that thought, Isabel could feel the dampness between her legs. Oh God. This was not good. She was going to lose her baby, Sidney's baby. She curled herself tightly around the life that was ebbing out of her and sobbed.

Chiswick returned just as another wracking pain shot through Isabel. Lying on the bed, facing the door, she gritted her teeth to keep from screaming, but nothing could prevent the tears flooding the pillow.

"Do not be melodramatic, Isabel. As soon as I have the money, I'll see that you're returned to your soldier." Chiswick shouldered the door shut and sauntered toward the bed.

Isabel closed her eyes. She might be able to bear the pain, but she did not think she could bear the idea of losing her unborn child while George Chiswick stood watching. "Please," she whispered.

"Please? A bit too late for pleading, my dear. Now, let us get you up and be on our way." Chiswick moved nearer the bed and stopped dead.

"What is this? Have you done yourself an injury?" He stared at the blood now staining the coverlet.

Isabel opened her eyes and turned a malevolent gaze on the man in front of her. "You have done me the injury."

"I never laid a hand on you. Now tell me what you've done." Isabel could see that Chiswick was frightened. But something must be done. She knew now it was too late to save her baby, but she needed to assure that she lived. She desperately needed to see Sidney again.

"I have lost my baby." Saying the words drove home the truth, and she choked on another sob. Gathering every bit of strength she had against another contraction, she tried to sit up.

"You fool. What have you done to me?" Chiswick's face was chalk white.

"Done to you? By all that's holy, George, please find me a physician." Isabel collapsed back onto the bed and watched as Chiswick's face was replaced with blackness.

Consciousness returned slowly. Isabel woke to find herself in a clean bed, dressed in a plain cotton shift. She tentatively tested how her body felt. The pain had subsided and she seemed to have stopped bleeding, but she felt ill . . . and empty. She knew with a dreadful certainty that her baby was no more.

An old woman sat beside the bed, wringing out a rag in a basin of water.

"Who are you?" Isabel asked.

"Mrs. Maynard. People here call me Mother." The woman finished wringing out the cloth and wiped Isabel's face. Only then did Isabel realize how hot she was.

"But . . ." Isabel couldn't seem to get any more words out.

The old woman moved to the edge of the bed and,

lifting Isabel's head, held a cup to her lips. Isabel gratefully let the cool water slide down her throat.

"I'm the midwife." Mother Maynard answered the unasked question. "Your gentleman friend sent for me."

It all flooded back, every moment until she had fainted. "Not my friend," Isabel said, shaking her head.

"Dare say not, seeing as he took himself off the minute I arrived. Leastways, he did send for me and here I am. But you've lost the little one." Mrs. Maynard moved back to her chair and dipped the rag into the basin.

Isabel's eyes filled with tears, and her hand went to her belly. "My baby."

"Probably not your last one. You're a good, strong girl, Mrs. . . .?"

"Chamberlayne," Isabel said, her thoughts flying to Sidney. He had not even known she carried his child, and now she had lost it in a foolish, foolish undertaking. Would he ever forgive her? Would she ever forgive herself?

The old woman leaned toward her with the damp cloth, but Isabel stilled her hand. "Will I die?" she asked. Would she die without telling Sidney she loved him? Might he never know?

"Likely not, if we can get your fever down. Now be a good girl and lie still. Try to sleep. I'll be here."

Isabel let her hand drop to the bed as Mrs. Maynard put the cloth on her forehead.

"Must send for my husband." Isabel was not sure if she had actually spoken the words.

"I told you, the gentleman left as soon as I got here." Mrs. Maynard's voice dripped with disgust.

Isabel managed a small smile. "He was not my husband. Sidney Chamberlayne . . . London . . . Please find him."

"London's a big place, Mrs. Chamberlayne."

"Bruton Place." Isabel's heart sank. Her head lolled back on the pillow, and she stared at the ceiling. Sidney was in Dover. How long before a messenger could reach him? She closed her eyes and inhaled a deep, determined sigh. Whenever he got here, she would be waiting for him.

Chapter 24

Sidney pulled his horse to a halt and waited until the approaching rider caught up to him. He had delayed leaving London for what seemed an interminable length of time. Impatient to find Isabel, Sidney had left before the man he had requested from Whitehall arrived.

Captain Sneed must not have been far behind him. He pulled his horse up beside Sidney just at the top of the rise into Stevenage.

"Glad you could make it." Sidney scanned the hills. The afternoon sun shone low over the barrows that lay beyond the little market town. Beside him, Captain Sneed nodded in agreement. Sidney was glad to see him. He had been in Sidney's regiment, and it was critical to have someone he could count on.

"How much farther do you think?" Sneed shaded his eyes and peered toward the barrows.

Sidney shook his head. "Not farther than Northampton, I hope." But that was just a prayer. He thought it more likely that Chiswick had packed Isabel up and continued his flight. But where would they go? It was obvious that Chiswick had been headed to Gretna Green with Julia. That made sense. What had Isabel offered the man in exchange for Julia, and where would Chiswick take her to collect it? The very thought that Chiswick's price might extend beyond money made

Sidney's skin crawl and his muscles tense. It was imperative he find Isabel before another day passed.

"What's that?" Sneed nodded up the road, where a curricle was rounding a bend.

Sidney squinted. It was not possible. Would Chiswick be foolish enough to bring Isabel back to London? In a curricle? "Over here," he said, turning his horse into a stand of beeches by the side of the road.

Sneed followed, and the two sat silently peering at the road through the leafy barrier. Within minutes, the dusty curricle approached their stand.

Sidney twisted in his saddle to get a good look at the driver. Although the sun was low on the horizon, the blond hair and classic features were unmistakable—Chiswick. But he was alone.

No Isabel. Sidney ruthlessly tamped down the panic coursing through his veins. He had not led his men safely back from battle by succumbing to emotion. First he would deal with the blackguard, and then he would find his wife.

Sidney nodded to his companion. They circled the trees back in the direction they had come and edged out from the cover of the branches directly in front of the curricle.

Chiswick's horse shied, and the light vehicle slewed to the right. Rising to scrabble for the reins, Chiswick lost his balance and toppled onto the center of the road while the curricle wobbled toward the verge. Sidney was out of his saddle and on the ground at the same moment. The difference was that Sidney was on his feet.

As Chiswick scrambled in the dirt, Sidney closed with him. Out of the corner of his eye, he could see Sneed dismount and gather the reins of the curricle, leading the horse and equipage to the road's edge. Then Sidney turned his full attention to the man in the road.

In one swift motion, Sidney reached down, grasped Chiswick's jacket and pulled him to his feet. He grabbed Chiswick's lapels in both hands and all but lifted him off the ground.

"Where is she?" Sidney's voice was like cold steel, and Chiswick gave him the satisfaction of cringing. Sidney shook him.

"Where is she?" he repeated.

Chiswick stared at him. Sidney could tell that he was considering what his next move would be. If he had any sense, he would realize that there was no use in dissembling. Sidney shook him again.

"I don't know what you mean. What is this all about?" Peering down at Sidney's hands, Chiswick struggled to look nonchalant.

"Don't make me hurt you."

Chiswick glanced quickly up at Sidney.

"Yes, I mean it," Sidney said harshly, his gaze never leaving his opponent.

Chiswick hesitated for one more moment before speaking. "Your wife, you mean?"

Sidney's voice was grim. "My wife. If she is hurt, I promise you will rue the day you first drew breath."

Chiswick paled.

Oh God. Something had happened to Isabel. Sidney could feel the blood rushing to his head and fought not to choke the man he held between his hands.

"Where is she?"

"She owes me money."

Good Lord. The man was totally without sense. Did he not understand that Sidney would happily cut him down where he stood if he could be sure it would not endanger Isabel?

"I will owe you something infinitely more painful if you do not tell me where she is." Sidney clenched his hands in the fabric of Chiswick's jacket and raised him off the ground.

"Northampton." The word came out on a gasp, and Sidney lowered him. "I swear. I did nothing to her."

Sidney chose not to address the latter statement. "Where in Northampton?"

Chiswick blinked, and Sidney gave him another shake.

"Rose and Crown." Chiswick spat out the name.

"Thank you." Sidney unwound his right hand from Chiswick's jacket, drew back his arm and punched the man in the jaw. He released the lapel he still held, and Chiswick dropped like a stone.

"What are you doing?" Sneed had abandoned the curricle and was looking down at the recumbent figure of their prime suspect.

"My hand slipped." Sidney rubbed his left hand across the knuckles of his right.

"Did he confess to carrying the money?" Sneed asked, shaking his head in disbelief.

"I didn't think to ask him. I think we should bind him, don't you?" Sidney reached out a toe and poked at Chiswick.

"Yes. Probably. Although he doesn't look as though he's going anywhere at the moment. What do you mean you didn't think to ask him?" Sneed went back to his horse and returned with a length of rope.

Sidney let out a long breath. "Left that to you, my friend. Let's tie him up, and you can take him back to London and do what must be done."

"And where are you going?" Sneed knelt and began wrapping the rope around Chiswick's wrists.

"God willing, to fetch my wife."

Isabel sat up against the pillows and drank from the cup Mother Maynard handed her. She made a face at the bitter taste.

"Willow bark," the old woman said. "Best thing I know for the fever."

Isabel tended to believe her. Sometime in the night, the relentless cycle of heat and chills had broken, and, for the first time, she thought she might see another day.

She drained the cup and handed it back to the midwife. Resting her head against the pillow, she closed her eyes and, for a moment, allowed her grief to take her. She had awakened several times during her fever to the cries of a child. Fever dreams. Her child that was not to be.

Tears leaked out from under Isabel's closed eyelids, and the old woman leaned forward and took her hand. "I know, dearie. I've lost them, too. It will get better, I promise."

Isabel's tears erupted into a loud sob, and the old woman slid onto the side of the bed and took her in her arms, rocking her and crooning.

"Isabel." Was this another fever dream? Isabel raised her head. Her husband, her Sidney, stood in the doorway, dusty, disheveled and altogether wonderful.

The old woman slipped off the bed and left the room as Isabel reached out toward her husband. "Sidney."

In a heartbeat, Sidney crossed the room, sat on the bed and took her in his arms. He was so warm, so solid, so reassuring. Isabel burrowed into him, snaking her arms under his open jacket and wrapping them tightly around his back. "Sidney."

As if sensing exactly what she needed, Sidney did not speak but enfolded her, sharing his warmth and strength, creating a shield against anything that might threaten her. She had never told him she loved him, and he had never said those words to her, but at this moment his arms told her everything she needed to know. She buried her face against his shoulder and let the tears come.

She could feel Sidney lower his head and his lips brush the top of her hair. Eventually he leaned back against the wall and tilted her chin up so that he was looking into her eyes.

"What happened, Isabel?"

His voice was so gentle that Isabel thought she might not be able to keep the tears away long enough to tell him. She bit down on the sob forming in her throat and looked into the fathomless brown eyes that had become so dear to her.

"I . . . I came after Julia," she said.

Sidney put a hand to her cheek, wiping away a tear with the pad of his thumb. "I know that, dearest. Julia returned to London at the same time I did, and I had it all from her and Louisa. Tell me what happened after you sent her home." Carefully, as if she might break, he dropped a soft kiss on her lips.

Isabel put her hand to her mouth, savoring the kiss, trying to keep it in place. Her gaze wandered over the hard planes of Sidney's face. Would their baby have looked like him?

"Our baby . . . Oh, Sidney." The tears began again.

"Our baby?"

"The carriage ride . . . It was too much . . . too hard. I lost our baby." Isabel watched his face, willing him not to hate her for what she had done.

"You never said." Sidney's voice conveyed no emotion and, for the first time since he arrived, Isabel was frightened.

"It was so early. And then you were gone. I wanted to be sure. And . . ." She drew a gasping breath, willing herself to stop crying. "And I wanted to tell you first that I love you."

Slowly, Sidney closed his eyes. The image of Isabel's lovely face and huge amber eyes, the tears streaking her unnaturally pale cheeks, the curtain of gold hair waving over her shoulders, was as vivid as it had been with his eyes open. Her face, Sidney realized, had been with him since before he left for Dover. She had been a part of him for longer than that.

Opening his eyes, he shifted his legs onto the bed. Carefully, he lifted Isabel and sat her across his lap. Carefully, he raised her head and placed another chaste kiss on her beautiful mouth.

"Are *you* well?" He could barely breathe as he waited for the answer.

"Mrs. Maynard says I am. But, oh, Sidney, our baby."

Sidney pressed her head to his shoulder and kissed her brow. His heart ached for her and the child neither would ever know. "I am so sorry, Isabel. I am sorry about our baby, and I am sorry I wasn't here when you needed me."

"I was so afraid I would die before I could tell you I loved you." Isabel's voice was barely a whisper.

"But you have told me." Sidney was stunned by the joy of that telling.

"Yes." Isabel snuggled into him, murmuring in what sounded like contentment.

"But Isabel . . ."

She looked up and Sidney could see the pain and trepidation still lurking in her eyes.

"I have something to tell you as well." He pulled her a little closer.

"I know," she said, nodding.

Sidney smiled down at Isabel, warmly nestled against his chest. His wife was a wonderful puzzle. "You know?"

"Your arms told me."

"Let me take you home, my love, and tell you again and again for the rest of our lives."

Their lips met and clung.

And when they broke the kiss, Sidney said the words. "I love you, Isabel."

Epílogue

Hampshire, September 1815

Isabel leaned back against her husband and gazed out onto the sprawling park in back of their country estate. The garden glowed with autumnal warmth in the setting sun. She sighed in deep contentment. Sidney's vital presence and his surprising aptitude for estate management had revitalized the estate and banished the last remnant of Isabel's former existence.

It seemed as though life could not be any better. Napoleon was aboard the *Northumberland*, bound for St. Helena, this time to be kept under heavy guard, and England was at peace. After extracting information from Chiswick that eventually led to his associates and directing the operation that had brought them all to trial, Sidney had resigned Whitehall for the life of a gentleman farmer. Isabel had gladly relinquished her life in London, not sorry to see the last of any of the gentlemen who had once sought her attention.

Isabel sighed again and felt Sidney's arms tighten around her. She leaned her head back against his shoulder. His season of farming had made him broader and harder, if such a thing were possible. She wondered that she had ever thought happiness required a title and a fortune. Her husband's arms were all she required to be happy and fulfilled. That and the little secret she had harbored for the last month.

Turning her head to nuzzle Sidney's chest, she slid his hands from her waist over her still-flat abdomen. "I have something to tell you," she whispered. Then she turned around in his arms and looked up into his brown, brown eyes.

Sidney's gut tightened as he examined his wife's shining countenance. Her golden hair shone in the setting sun, and her amber eyes glowed with an inner light. He knew immediately what she meant.

He raised his hands and cupped her face, brushing a gentle kiss across her full lips. "When?"

"Before the next harvest." Isabel's hand slid from his chest and came to rest on her stomach. Sidney moved his hand to cover it.

"Isabel." Sidney did not know what else to say. Each day with Isabel was a delight, and the prospect of their child overwhelmed him. He leaned down and said everything with his kiss.

"It is the second-best gift I have ever received," Isabel said when their kiss finally ended.

"Only the second best?"

"Yes. The first best is your love."

And a new kiss began.

More Regency Romance
From Zebra

More Historical Romance From
Jo Ann Ferguson